The Storytellers Anthology Project

Stories We Tell

Tales from the
Story Circle of the Capital District

Storytellers

Siri Allison	Kate Dudding	Claire Nolan
Claire Beetlestone	Margaret French	Colette Odell
Kent Busman	Marni Gillard	Gil Payette
Janet Carter	Jeannine Laverty	Sandor Schuman
Betty Cassidy	Bonnie Mion	Maggie Whelan
Lâle Davidson	Merideth Nieves	Frank Wind
Alden (Joe) Doolittle	Eliud Nieves De La Rosa	

Edited by Sandor Schuman

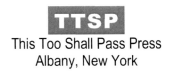

This Too Shall Pass Press
Albany, New York

Cover Art:
Story Circle of the Capital District
by Gil Payette, Storyteller

A skyline is surrounded by circular lines, a growing circle.
The image is of New York State's capital city, Albany.
Together they are representative of the
growing Story Circle of the Capital District.

ISBN-10: 098862852X
ISBN-13: 978-0-9886285-2-6

The Storytellers Anthology Project
www.storytellersanthology.com
sap@exedes.com

This Too Shall Pass Press
Albany, New York

Table of Contents

About Story Circle

The genesis of our story circle came about at Jeannine Laverty's storytelling workshop at Great Camp Sagamore in Raquette Lake, New York. Lois Foight Hodges, Nancy Gifford, and Becky Holder established the Story Circle of the Capital District of New York State in 1983 and gathered a small group of folks who loved stories and storytelling. Together they discovered the power of this age-old tradition to build community, improve teaching, and communicate important ideas.

Members tell their stories to people of all ages. They tell in parks, museums, and nursing homes; in libraries, schools, and coffeehouses; in religious settings, art galleries, and colleges; at public meetings and at corporate and community events; at birthday parties, weddings and anniversaries—wherever adults or children or families gather to enjoy a spellbinding tale.

Story Circle has grown to a regional group of over 50 story-tellers and friends and offers support and development for storytellers through monthly meetings, workshops and advocacy efforts. In 1998 Story Circle launched a production arm to sponsor the annual Tellabration and the successful Story Sundays series at the historic Glen Sanders Mansion in Scotia, New York. In 2006, Story Circle began a partnership with Proctors Theatre in Schenectady, New York, as a resident company. The partnership offers Word Plays, a storytelling series at the theater, other productions throughout the community, and Story by Story, a public access television program.

More information on Story Circle, current productions and learning opportunities can be found at www.story-circle.org.

This collection of stories by twenty of our members is our first. We appreciate each teller's efforts to turn *told* stories into written ones, Sandy Schuman's efforts to initiate and coordinate this project, and Robyn Ringler's work to edit our final versions. We appreciate the work of all of our members who tell stories and enrich the world. And most of all, we appreciate you, our listeners and readers. Without you, we would not be storytellers.

Alden (Joe) Doolittle
On behalf of the Story Circle of the Capital District
November 2014

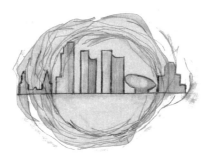

Stories We Tell

Siri Allison

 Siri has always been captivated by stories. As a child, she brought stacks of books home from the library and spent hours reading. Then she discovered another form of story, theater. She majored in acting and spent several years following the theatrical muse. When her children were in elementary school, she began telling stories and leading creative dramatics in schools, eventually developing curriculum-enhancing residencies for all elementary grade levels. In 2005, her family moved to upstate New York, and Siri discovered the wonderful tellers at Story Circle. From them she has learned to tell to adult audiences, and experienced the power of stories resonating with each other in performance. She now tells stories around the region.

Siri Allison
Salem, New York
siriallison.blogspot.com
siristory@earthlink.net

East River Angels

Siri Allison

I actually forgot about this incident until a few years ago. My husband spoke of it one day and the memory came flooding back. I'm glad to know he remembered it too; otherwise, I might think I had dreamed the whole thing.

In our younger years, my husband Michael and I lived on East 18th Street in New York City. On Saturday mornings, I would sometimes go out for a run. I wasn't a serious runner. A "run" meant a slow jog interspersed with walking. Really, it was just a way to get some movement and fresh air.

The closest place for such an outing was East River Park. The sidewalk there was sandwiched between the cold, gray East River on one side and the busy FDR Drive on the other. Beyond FDR Drive loomed the housing projects and drug dealers of Alphabet City. In those days, it wasn't the safest neighborhood. But one thing I loved about New York was all the different kinds of people that lived there, and the park was a welcome spot of green, and it was close to home—so I went anyway, figuring that there were always kids playing nearby and I'd keep my wits about me.

One fine spring morning I headed out. It was a gorgeous blue sunny day—the first day warm enough to wear shorts. I made my way down to 12th Street, took the access bridge over to the park, and started jogging down the sidewalk. Surprisingly for such a beautiful day, the park was eerily empty. Not one person in sight. *Oh well*, I thought, *surely people will show up soon. I'll remember my rule: keep my wits about me.*

I hadn't gone too far when I stumbled and fell. I hauled myself right up and assessed the damage. The front of my shin was scraped and there was a cut on my knee. It didn't hurt that much, but it was bleeding like crazy. Blood flowed down my leg into my little white socks. At least there hadn't been anyone around to see me take such an embarrassing fall. I turned around and hobbled back up the sidewalk towards home.

But my knee kept bleeding profusely. Of course—what did I expect?—I was *walking*. So when I came to a little enclosure with benches, I stopped. In my memory, this enclosure had the river as its outer border, cobblestone or brick on the ground, and several benches, backed by a low decorative fence around the entire periphery. The fence opened up onto the sidewalk near the path to the access bridge over FDR Drive. It was just the place to rest. So there I stood, stretching my leg out onto a bench trying to stop the bleeding.

After a moment, I looked up and saw a homeless man approaching. He wore two or three coats, a scarf and hat (odd, because, remember, it was warm enough to wear shorts) and he carried several overstuffed plastic bags. I was on speaking terms with several street people and not generally afraid, but I did not know this particular guy or his mental state. There was no one else in sight and I was trapped by the river and the fence of the enclosure. *Where were my wits?* I tried to collect them. He shuffled right up.

Art by Hilary Allison

"Hi," I said.

"Hello," he said. "Would you like some Kleenex?"

"Thank you," I said, not knowing if he would hand me *clean* Kleenex. But he did. He reached in his pocket and handed me a generous wad of clean Kleenex.

"Thank you," I said.

"I always keep some of this around," he said. "The places I go, I need it." Then he left.

I mopped my leg for a minute. When I looked up, I saw another man approaching from the Lower East Side part of the river, where Mafia types pushed each other into the river with cement overshoes. He was short and stocky, wore a tan trench coat, black hat, black pants, black shoes, and carried a long black suitcase. In the movies, the suitcase would have contained a million dollars in unmarked bills or a tommy gun. He did not smile. And he was walking straight toward me.

"Hello," I said.

"Hello," he said. "Would you like some antibiotic cream?"

"Yes, thank you," I said.

He opened his suitcase, which contained not a tommy gun, but a trumpet. From a small compartment, he took out a tube of antibiotic cream and squirted a little onto my finger. He said he was tired because he'd been up all night playing his horn, and then walked away.

I rubbed the cream into my cut and continued to dab with the Kleenex. The bleeding was definitely slowing.

Suddenly, a huge bicycle came whizzing down into the park from the access path. On it was an extremely tall, strappingly muscular, decked-out dude, dressed head to toe in black leather. His jacket was covered in skulls, spikes and silver rivets. When he saw me, he turned and rode up, blocking the opening in the fence. He put one giant foot down on the pavement and still he towered over me.

"Hello," he said.

"Hello."

"Would you like a Band-Aid?"

"Oh no, thank you, I don't really need a Band-Aid."

"Oh, sure, take one. I've got plenty." He unzipped his bike pouch and handed me a Band-Aid.

"Thank you."

"Anytime." He smiled and cycled away.

So I stuck on the Band-Aid, decided my leg was respectable enough to pass through the city sidewalks, and limped my way home.

I thought then, and looking back on it, I also think now, that maybe that homeless man, that Mafia musician, and that huge cyclist were angels. If they weren't actually angels, some higher power must certainly have orchestrated their presence on that pathway to send me a message. This message was—in fact, the message still is—that I don't need to worry as much as I tend to, about myself or those I love, because in the unlikeliest of circumstances, we are being taken care of.

When Eve Got Lonesome

An African-American tale, recorded in David Cohn's, *Where I was Born and Raised* (1947), a book about the Mississippi Delta

Retold by Siri Allison

Adam and Eve, as everybody knows, were the first people in the world. They were perfectly happy. They had 40 acres of good bottom land. The weather was ideal: sunny and breezy with a spice of rain. The cow was pleased to give milk and the chickens wanted to give eggs. Adam played the guitar at night after supper. Eve loved to sing. They laughed at each other's jokes. Everything was just perfect—except for one thing.

Next to Eve, what Adam loved most was to go off hunting and fishing. Sometimes his hunting and fishing trips lasted two or three days. While he was gone, Eve, of course, had no one to talk to. There *was* nobody else.

On one such occasion, when Adam was gone three days, Eve got just too lonesome. When Adam came back, she said, "Adam, when you're gone I've got no one to talk to. I get too lonesome. So, from now on, I don't want you to go away anymore unless you can find somebody else for me to talk to."

This made Adam sad. He thought and figured and thought some more. What to do? He was still thinking about it the next day as he walked along the road. And there, who should he meet but the Lord?

"Morning, Lord!"

"Morning, Adam. How are you today?"

"Oh, fine, thank you, Lord. You've given us so much. Eve and I are happy, and the farm is doing well. We are both very, very grateful. But today, there is just one little problem."

"Oh? What's that, Adam?"

"Well, Lord, you know I love to go off hunting and fishing. But when I'm gone, Eve is lonesome. She has no one to talk to. So, I was wondering, Lord, could you make some more people?"

9

"Well, I suppose I could. When would you like this done?"

"How about this evening?"

The Lord pulled out his diary and checked it. There were no big storms or earthquakes scheduled for that night. "Tonight would be fine," he said. "Meet me at the creek bank after supper and we'll make some new people."

Right after supper Adam hurried over to the creek bank. The Lord had Adam cut down saplings and bend them into shape, and then the Lord took clay from the creek bank and patted it onto the sapling forms and made people. He made short ones, tall ones, fat ones, skinny ones, black ones, white ones, mixed-up ones: all races and colors. When each person was finished, he set him or her up against the fence to dry. All together, lined up like that, they looked real nice, all those different shapes and colors.

But it was getting dark. The Lord said, "Adam, it's getting too dark to see. Go home and get some rest. Meet Me back here in the morning and we'll finish up these people. We'll put some brains in them."

Adam went home. At sunup the next morning he hurried back to the creek bank. But he found himself looking at an *empty* fence. All those people had just gotten up and walked off without waiting for the Lord to put their brains in!

And they have been repopulating the Earth ever since.

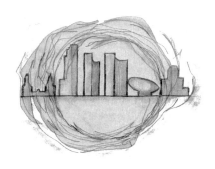

Claire Beetlestone

Dr. Beetlestone was born into a family whose members were musicians, artists, writers and actors by night, and teachers, journalists, CPAs and psychologists by day. Dr. B. follows right in their footsteps. Mother of five, she has been a docent to a tropical zoo, a dancer, and an art impresario. She is a practicing specialist physician who calls Cooperstown, New York or Argyle, Scotland home. She continues to travel alone in Africa, Asia, and Europe, making friends along the way, listening to their stories, and making sure to leave a few of her own wherever she goes.

Claire Beetlestone
Cooperstown, New York
cbeetlestone2003@yahoo.com
607-547-9067

Red Bird

Claire Beetlestone

Fire stretched the horizon.
The dusty land of great thirst was burning.
Then the rains came.
EXPLODED swift, hard and wild.

The land rejoiced.
Racing streams flooded dry lake beds.
New water was clear and shining.
Gao Yth'sai knelt down to drink, finally, to drink deep.
It was then that he saw the reflection of the Red Bird.

He looked up to the sky.
The bird was gone.

From that moment until the end.
Gao Yth'sai wanted the Red Bird for his own.

Gao Yth'sai the youth wanted the bird for his own.
Gao Yth'sai the hunter wanted the bird for his own.
Gao Yth'sai killer of the Giant Bull Eland wanted the bird for his own.
Gao Yth'sai in the lust of youth wanted the bird for his own.
Gao Yth'sai the trance dancer, the healer, wanted the bird for his own.
Gao Yth'sai the covetous wanted the bird for his own.

His eyes burned for the sight of the Red Bird.
His whole being cried out for the bird.

So he started running as only a Kalahari hunter can run.
An unhurrying chase.
An unperturbed pace.
Deliberate speed.
Majestic instancy.

He followed the rumour of the Red Bird
In the half-remembered dream of a child,
In the vision of a fever,

In the ranting of a madman,
In the gossip of the market place,
In the camps of camel caravans,
In the tales of the salt slaves.

He ran down the nights and the days,
Down the arches of the years.
Always moving, always asking.

He ran on
as only a Kalahari hunter can run.

Gao Yth'sai, the runner, was old
When he came to the desert market
To meet the seller of Frankincense.

The merchant was bent, long fingers and nose,
All angles.
But strong under his strip-cloth garment
Shrewd eyes burned under bushy white eyebrows,
His beard tucked carefully into his waistband.

He had come through the Empty Quarter
Then to green rain-soaked, fog-shrouded mountains
To fetch the resin.
Then to the great northern desert to sell the precious Frankincense.

He had taken his camels over all the trade routes
From the vast waters to the mountains at Earth's end.
He knew much.

He knew where the Red Bird lived
And carefully instructed Gao Yth'sai,
How to go, which star to follow,
Which valleys never to enter
To reach the mountain of rock
That rose high and solitary above the plain.
The home of the Red Bird was at the summit.

Gao Yth'sai continued running,
Running to see the bird again.

He ran as only a Kalahari hunter can run
An unhurrying chase.
An unperturbed pace.
Deliberate speed.
Majestic instancy.

He found the mountain
Rising straight up.
Twice he circled one way,
Seeking a foothold, a handhold,
Twice he circled the other way.
The rock face was smooth and sheer, impossible.

But, down near the base was a small hole.
He cleared earth, widening, making a way
For his hands at first.
Then he dug until his small body could slip easily down into
empty dark.
Down, not up, into the rock.

His hands followed the inside wall all the way around.
The mountain was hollow!
He reached up, the wall continued jagged,
He began to climb.
Pieces of rock broke off, and fell
Rolling, thundering, echoing and reechoing
Filling the space with deafening roars as they hit the ground
GaoYth'sai knew then that his entrance was buried.
He could not get out that way.

It was dark, a darkness he had never known,
For the first time in his life, he knew fear.
He was a man of the desert, of the open space and the clear air.

Still he climbed, for an hour, a day, a lifetime
Carefully feeling for each handhold, testing each foothold
Slowly creeping upward.

Then he saw a glimmer far above. His eyes never left that light.
Renewed, he struggled, eyes unblinking toward that light.

Until weak, breathless he pulled himself over the lip of the chimney
and collapsed.
There was water collected in a small hollow up there.
He lapped a few drops
He could barely turn over to face the sky.
When he lay on his back
The brightness of the sun blinded him.
He closed his eyes for the last time.

As his body relaxed,
His right hand opened
And a single red feather floated down into it.

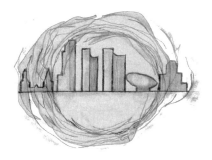

The Storm and the Stranger

Claire Beetlestone

This is really a very old, old story, told many times.
It has been told over the centuries.
It has been told in every part of the world where men go to fish the sea.

It may have happened last week or at anytime during the last three millennia.
But, to be told, the story must be placed somewhere.
So, I have placed it in the Hebrides off Scotland, off the isle of Barra.

It was a calm day
And the herring were running.
The favorable weather promised good fishing.
One hundred boats went out from the islands.

The fishermen started well before dawn, the stars were bright.
But by afternoon a storm-coming sky covered all.
By evening the North Westerly Wind freshened.
By midnight the weather was deteriorating rapidly
with strengthening winds
and heavy seas.

Most hauled in their nets and made for shelter.
Only a few decided to weather the storm.
Brendan's crew stayed out
for the boat was strong and the hold not yet filled.

Up on the hill, in the little whitewashed stone house in Barra,
The children were already asleep.
Brendan's Katriona waited.
Silently, keeping the ancient vigil for men who had fished the sea
Since the first boat was launched.

The local wireless stations operating only by day had shut down.
The BBC reported gales of 90 to 140 miles per hour.
Factory roofs had blown off sailing in the wind.

17

The rain was torrential,
Trains were stopped, tracks were flooded and covered with debris.
Foaming tidal surges crossed Orkney and the Shetlands.
Water had traveled as far as two miles inland
flooding entire streets of little fishing villages
damaging sea walls and undermining the coast.

BBC reported that warnings could not penetrate the
flood-threatened areas
Because many electric lines were down.

Then Katriona's own electricity failed.
The wireless was dead.

And she had heard nothing yet of the fate of the fishing boats.

She took the paraffin lamp, the Tilley lamp,
out of the alcove by the peat fire,
trimmed the wick and lit it, that same lamp had hissed and glared
through the vigils of three generations of women.

Katriona's mother had kept it lit
during the vigil for Katriona's father.
Katriona's mother's mother had kept it lit
during the vigil for Katriona's grandfather.

In the shadows cast by the light of that old Tilley lamp
she could almost see the images of the women
waiting at the shore in the wake of the storm.
Each waiting for her man to wash up
drowned, heavy, stiff, and water logged,
His face still recognizable! The sea of the Western Isles is so cold.

As each of the drowned appeared, helping hands would carry him
up to his house
where he would be washed, clothed in the winding sheet, and laid out.
Katriona remembered.

She kept the vigil, silently waiting,
Still against the night.

The wind and rain never ceased.
Katriona threw more peat on the fire.

Then she looked in on the bairns, Fiona and little Edwin,
and remembered her mother's song.

Sleep on, your father's late tonight …
He's out beyond where the mermaids are
and the whale
and the sunken ship…

The dawn came. Wind and rain never ceased.
The children stayed quiet, with grave eyes.

This was a strange time,
a time of deepening dread
A time filled with damp monotony and even boredom
A time punctuated with surging moments of fright.

On the third day, when the storm began to wane,
Muttering and moaning in its death throes
There came a thumping at the door.
Katriona opened to a dark bedraggled stranger
sagging against the door jam
And while the door thudded open and closed in the wind
They pulled him in.
And with some difficulty they managed to arrange him in the
chair near the fire.

Edwin fetched a towel, for the rain had soaked through his cap.
While streams of water ran down his face and the back of his neck
Fiona rubbed dry his thick tangled white hair and beard.
His heavy coat they spread out near the fire,
it began to steam as it dried.
They wrestled off his boots and emptied them.
And, as best they could, they wrapped him in a blanket.
He was barely conscious. His limbs were ice cold.

Katriona ladled out some of the Scotch broth.
That balsamic broth ever-simmering over the fire
replenished daily with barley, carrots, onions and occasional

scraps of mutton.
Fiona fed him sips from a large spoon much as you would a child.
Soon he seemed to smile
but could still say nothing in his exhaustion.
He fell asleep in the chair beside the fire.
The three watched over and gently attended
to the silent stranger.

Later in the evening he stirred, opened his eyes
Still he would not speak
But they got him to table
They put food in the eating place, drink in the drinking place
And then led him to sleep in the sleeping place.

During the night the winds fell and the rain turned to mist.
And in the morning,
Brendan came home,
wet and weary, with a tale to tell.
When the tale was told and the welcome done
They all went in to show him the silent stranger
Who awoke and sat up at first blinking in confusion.

Then, both Brendan and the stranger stayed stock still
and looked at each other for a long moment
Their eyes filling with tears
And Brendan fell to his knees to embrace the stranger
with passion and, at once, tenderness.

"This" he sobbed, "this is Father Murdoch whom we had
thought to have been lost to the sea these many years ago."

So now listeners be reminded of the verse in Hebrews 13:2

Be not forgetful to entertain strangers
For thereby
Some have entertained angels unawares.

Murdoch's journey had been long,
Shipwrecked, then cast up on foreign shores broken and bereft,
He healed and eked out a life there,

A life filled with hardship, danger, misery, generosity, and finally triumph.

But that is a story for another time.

Murdoch had come home to Barra.

Kent Busman

Kent Busman is the Executive Director of Camp Fowler where storytelling is an integral part of helping campers and adults interpret their experiences in the woods and lakes of the Adirondack Mountains. Kent is also an ordained minister in the Reformed Church in America. Kent has told stories in schools, churches, and campgrounds as well as led workshops on sharing stories for Christian educators.

Kent Busman
Scotia, New York
kent.busman@gmail.com
315-877-5660

The Lost Tools of Schoharie

Kent Busman

Down in my basement, which I call my "shop," I have a toolbox I made about twenty years ago out of some scrap lumber. It's two feet long—long g enough to hold a carpenter's square. The handle is an old broom handle cut to fit with a leather strap I use to carry it when it gets heavy. Normally my toolbox sits down in my shop and I'll take it out when I'm going to work on stuff around the house. My guess is that most people's toolboxes live in similar places and they don't get out much.

But that changed for thousands of toolboxes on August 28, 2011 when the Schoharie Creek, just a little meandering stream, was flooded by Hurricane Irene. This little creek, not wider than a good-sized barn, flooded to over a mile across and wiped out the towns of Prattsville, Middleburgh and Schoharie. When the water reached about six feet high, people from surrounding towns grabbed their toolboxes and headed to Schoharie.

At that point I didn't really know what tools I was going to need. I just threw in every assortment of tool I could think of: tool belt, squares, level—and just ran.

The first couple of weeks we didn't need our toolboxes much. It was all muck. We needed five-gallon buckets. We'd go down into people's basements where they kept all their stuff: canning jars and pre-rusted tools. We would fill up the buckets and carry the sludge out and pile it in the street along with all the keepsakes and treasures that didn't survive. I would be crouched down in those spaces where the mold was already growing. And I would sing out of the irony of the entire situation. Because I knew that my life was ebbing away with each trip down, but I did it anyway. And hundreds of people kept going down.

Slowly, as the muck receded, the work started to change and we began to use our toolboxes. The first time I got to use my toolbox was at Moe's house. Moe had lost all the flooring in his living room and it needed to be replaced. Our job was to get underneath and put insulation in before we put the flooring down so the living room would stay warmer in the wintertime. My buddy Bruce and I tried to figure out how we were going to do this.

There were two ways to do projects in Schoharie. The first way was to work as fast as you could to get the work done so you could move on to the next house. The second way was to work as though you were working for your best friend and strive to make this the best house ever. Nobody worked the first way.

"All we have to do is tear up one of the floor joists and you can crawl under there," said my buddy Bruce. "And I'll hand you the insulation so you can nail it up from below." Now I'm the youngest child. I know what it's like to get stuck with that job. So I would go down under Moe's floor and nail that insulation in. Every now and again I'd come up for air. (Two high school kids joined us. They didn't do anything, but they were so excited to help.)

After we had sealed up the floor and finished, I realized that I was missing my little nail set from my tool belt. This was my first lost tool of Schoharie.

My second lost tool was a four-foot drywall square. I was working with two guys, Jeff and Neil. You never really knew who you were going to be working with, but I will never forget these two. I was tearing up a floor in one room, while they hung drywall in the next room over. And I heard something I never thought I would hear on a work site. "Hey Jeff, do you have your lipstick?" said Neil.

"Why yes, Neil, I do!" Jeff responded. "It's cherry red. Is that okay?"

"That's my favorite," said Neil.

I'm an open-minded guy, but that one threw me. I cautiously peered around the corner and saw them putting the lipstick on an outlet box to mark where to cut the drywall. I'm going to borrow lipstick next time I hang drywall. I got so excited about this new trick that when we packed up at the end of the day, I completely forgot my drywall square. It was lost in Schoharie.

Other people lost tools in Schoharie too. And sometimes they lost them to me! One day, I was working with a guy named Jack. Finally, it was my turn to start hanging drywall and we were finishing this beautiful sitting room. Well, Jack was what I would call a "serial cusser." Every other word out of his mouth was "cussin' this" and "cussin' that." It wasn't because he was mean or tough. He just used swear words to fill in the spaces of his thoughts. I liked that about him.

After a morning of work, he came over to me and said, "So what is it that you do?"

I looked up from where I was kneeling on the floor and, with a wry smile, I simply said, "Jack, I'm a minister."

"No shit!" said Jack. The rest of the day he never swore, which was sad for me, but I guess it was Jack's way of saying I was doing a good job.

Jack had a tool you could put on your drill that would allow you to drive in drywall screws but stop them before they went in too deep. It was called a *dimpler* and I had never heard of such a wonderful thing. To a minister, this was the next best thing to Jesus coming back because it made that drywall look so good. And we were hanging drywall as though our best friend lived in that house.

At the end of the day, Jack looked at me and said, "I still can't believe you're a minister." He held out his hand to shake mine and, as we shook, he put the *dimpler* in my palm. It lives in my toolbox now.

I picked up and lost other things. I found a random hammer in my toolbox once. I lost a little hand square. One day we were doing a blitz on the parsonage of a young clergy couple in Prattsville. There were about forty of us. Toolboxes everywhere. When you're working like that, you don't have a toolbox, the group sort of has a toolbox. It's really kind of a beautiful thing. And I had that hammer I found and was working in one room and got called into another room. I set that hammer in the wall. Turns out I got delayed in the other room and when I returned twenty minutes later, the wall was covered over and my hammer was lost. It's still living inside that wall.

When you work in Schoharie and the Presbyterian Church bell rings at noon, you set your tools down and meander towards the Reformed Church where the lunch site is. The dusty, muddy workers mimic the Schoharie Creek on a kinder day, flowing slowly along.

Every day, volunteers came from I know not where and brought food from who knows who and prepared lunch for us. We all sat at tables together, unlikely comrades in this task. A crew came up from North Carolina for a week and Mennonites traveled from the Midwest. There were folks who got the day off from IBM, the women's team from Rensselaer, and even Mormons from Salt Lake City—who were lousy painters, but wonderful men.

I lost my favorite tool going to lunch one day. It was a 32-ounce, 18-inch long, waffle-headed rig ax—a framing hammer whose backside looked sort of like a hatchet. I loved that tool and we did some serious work together.

In this one particular house, that 32-ounce, 18-inch long hammer was great for knocking all of the cabinets out. That was good, therapeutic work, swinging away pondering questions like: *Why do bad things happen to good people?* and *What will we do when Schoharie floods again?*

I was working with the four masked women from Rensselaer that day. I never knew their names and never saw them without their masks. I thought I could get held up and robbed at any moment all day! As soon as we got the wood out to the curb, the convicts, who really may have been robbers in a former life, loaded that lumber into the trucks to haul it away.

I set my hammer down when I heard the Presbyterian Church bell. And when I got back from lunch, my hammer was gone. Scooped up with the detritus and loaded with other lost treasures. A loss that pales alongside the tragedy of a flooded town. A lot of people lost a lot of things in Schoharie.

I worry about Schoharie. Not that it won't get fixed up. It will. People are still picking up their toolboxes and coming. I'm worried about the town. Because I fear the day will come when the Presbyterian Church bell will ring and only the Presbyterians will come. And I worry that when we sit down to eat we will make up stories about why we shouldn't eat with people who are different from us. I worry that we will forget how beautifully we all worked together.

But then I remember the lost tools. And I know the lost tools won't forget. We will hear whispering from beneath our floors, or from inside our walls. We will hear whispers from our toolboxes stored once again in our basements or garages. And I pray that we will once again open our ears to hear.

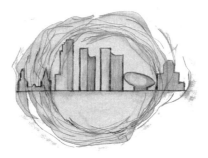

Janet Carter

Janet Carter's acting past shows in her love of character and dialogue. As a teller, she's performed at retreats, domestic violence shelters, libraries and senior centers. The Winter Lights Festival in the Capital District welcomed a story about "The Troubles" in Northern Ireland and a variety of audiences have responded to her tales of a southern family of long ago. The establishment of an ongoing story telling venue in Saugerties, New York is perhaps her most lasting contribution. Aided by a wide variety of talented colleagues, "Stories for Inquiring Minds" is four years old and counting.

Janet Carter
Saugerties, New York
janet.carter332@gmail.com

Tea Dance
Knoxville, Tennessee, 1914

Janet Carter

Isabel stood for just a moment in the hallway outside the ballroom of the Knoxville Ladies Club. She could see the late afternoon sun streaming into the large chandeliered room, hear the orchestra tuning up, smell the scent of the evening roses drifting through the open windows and feel the stirring of excitement among those already lining the walls—the tea dance would begin soon. Her gaze rested on Mrs. McIver, a commanding presence in the chaperones' corner. Isabel wondered what it would be like to be old, to have such a bosom and wear an impervious corset.

"Isabel, Isa-*bel*, where have you been? I've been looking all over for you!"

Isabel smiled at the flurry that always attended her friend's arrival. "Oh Nellie Mae, you look beautiful!"

"Oh Isabel, *Isabel*, guess who's here in time for the tea dance? John Franklin, home from Davidson—I saw him coming up from the train, swinging his suitcase!" The sheer joy of it was almost more than could be conveyed. "I was in my room, Mamie had brought in my dress, and I saw him and then—oh, do you know what? Momma came in just at that moment! And she said, 'Nellie Mae Frazier, what are you doing standing at the window in your wrapper, like some Mary McGee just off the boat!' And I said, 'Oh, yes, ma'am, but I do believe that's John Franklin Keith coming up from the station home from college. She bustled over and said, 'Oh-h, let me see!'"

The two girls giggled. Consternation showed in Nellie Mae's voice when she said, "Oh, Isabel, if he doesn't sign my dance card, I don't know what I'll do."

Isabel, reassuring as always, said, "He will, Nellie Mae, he will. Let's go in now." And the two friends locked arms and entered the room that contained their futures. Isabel, being Isabel, turned aside to speak to the chaperone. "Thank you, Mrs. McIver, for making this evening possible for us—we appreciate it."

A young man stepped forward. "Mrs. McIver." He ducked his head quickly, and then addressed the object of his interest. "Miss Gordon, I do believe this is my dance." And Isabel picked up the overskirt of her green dress and stepped out onto the dance floor as the music swelled. *Oh, what could be better than to be young and pretty and dancing?*

Mrs. McIver, watching, spoke to the other chaperones in a manner that brooked no contradiction. "Now, there is a well brought up young woman; I don't care if her people are from Michigan."

The couples circled the floor. Isabel happily saw, over her partner's shoulder, a glowing Nellie Mae join the dancers with the white-evening-jacketed John Franklin. Oh, he was handsome for sure.

The evening progressed as it should, the young women beautiful and the young men gallant. Isabel moved past the sparkling tea table in a happy trance.

Then something happened that she would remember all her life. The orchestra seemed to fall silent—how could that be? Conversation seemed to cease. She watched John Franklin take a cup of tea—doubtless for Nellie Mae—from the hand of Jim, Mrs. McIver's yard boy, brought over to help with the service. A white man being served by a black man; nothing unusual in that. But—the profiles were the same. And there was something about the set of the shoulders. Jim was wearing a white serving jacket for the evening—is that what triggered the comparison? A white jacket facing a white jacket. They are brothers, she thought suddenly. Half-brothers. Something unknown, unallowed, not to be mentioned was there before her, something she had never before been asked to comprehend. She and now all the others were staring at something they didn't want to see. Then the music asserted itself and they were dancing again.

Much later, when the good-byes had been said and the thanks properly expressed, Isabel and four close friends settled themselves for the night on the third floor of Nellie Mae's house. They had hung up their ball dresses and let down their hair, ready for the all-engrossing, post-dance discussion. Mrs. Frazier had called up the stairs, "Young ladies, some people in this house plan to sleep tonight. Turn the lamps down now."

In the darkness that followed, the atmosphere changed. Isabel lay listening as someone began to cry. "It was an uncle, I always heard it was an uncle," said a tear-choked voice. Others were weeping now. And Isabel, being Isabel, thought, *They're crying for their lost families, the brothers and sisters they'll never know.* The less-generous hearted might have suggested that the girls were contemplating their futures. What was the price to be paid for being among the genteelly married?

Isabel felt her love for them and her separateness too. In that moment, with a strange clarity, she had discovered something. She was not going to stay in Knoxville; she was not going to end her life here within this circle of the embossed lie.

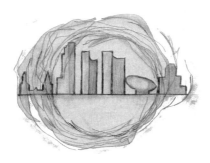

Betty Cassidy

Betty Cassidy began her storytelling career while teaching speech classes at SUNY Adirondack where she was a member of the English Department. Helping students find the stories they needed to support their speeches led her to discover her enthusiasm for presenting her own stories.

As an active member of the Story Circle of the Capital District, Betty has performed at Caffè Lena, Proctors Theater and various other venues. She has led memoir and storytelling workshops and presented yearly performances for the Academy of Lifelong Learning in Saratoga. Betty was the recipient of a grant from the Alfred Z. Solomon Charitable Trust which has allowed her to work with others to introduce the art of storytelling in workshops throughout the area. Betty feels lucky to have found a new and challenging career in storytelling.

Betty Cassidy
Saratoga Springs, New York
betcass@aol.com
518-306-4072
518-260-2140

The Letters

Betty Cassidy

In the small dining room, a three-foot-high map spread almost across the whole back wall. This was a map of the world as it existed in 1944. If you took a close look, you could see colored thumb tacks marking spaces up and down the east coast of America, across to Chicago, over to San Diego and trickling off after Hawaii. Every day Mary and her four little children would stare at this map and wonder where her husband was since the last tack had been added. The older children would stretch their fingers to trace the line of colored metal markers. Pat had been drafted into World War II late in 1943. Even though he was considered too old to be drafted at age 35, the war was intense and more and more recruits were needed. So Pat was in the US Navy, somewhere on a small ship, the LSM 139, as part of the Pacific fleet.

Mary stayed at home with four little children from the baby to her six-year-old. Life was hard for women in those days. Helpers like automatic washing machines, dryers and dishwashers didn't exist. Coal had to be shoveled into the furnace all winter, a garden planted and weeded all summer and grass cut with a push mower. Mary hauled wet clothes up from the wringer washing machine in the basement and hung them outside to dry. She had to handle these chores, and also be the parent to her children, while trying to stretch the small allotment the Navy sent each month to cover all their expenses. And, of course, the hardest thing she had to face was her loneliness and her fear for Pat's safety. Day after day her mind went through a series of "What if" questions: *Was he safe? Where was his ship now? When would he ever come home? Could she keep going alone?*

The one thing that helped Mary the most was the daily mail delivery. Joe, the mailman, had been bringing the mail down their street for years and he knew how Mary waited for Pat's letters. When one did arrive, she would read and reread it. The letters came on what was called "V Mail," a thin piece of paper that one could write on and then fold over so it would become its own envelope. Sometimes large sections of the letters would be blacked out by censors who did not allow classified information to be revealed. This didn't bother Mary as long as she could read "My Dear Mary" at the beginning and "Give the kids a hug and kiss from me. I love you. Pat" at the end. Some nights when she was feeling especially lonely, she would take out all the letters Pat had written during his many months away and read some of them to the children like a bedtime story. They were lulled to sleep as her soft voice read about life on a tiny ship in a vast ocean.

One week there was a letter on Monday and then nothing the rest of the week. Mary stopped Joe on Friday as he neared her house. "Are you sure there's no letter for me today?"

"Now, Mary, lots of times mail gets held up. Don't worry. We know Pat's a tough guy. He'll be fine. And you'll probably get two or three letters next week."

But there were no letters the next week. And none the following week. Day after day Mary would watch for Joe to turn the corner and head down her street. She prayed there would be a letter. Nothing came but a few bills and a letter from her sister. Joe hated to have to walk by every day and see the pain on Mary's face. It had been six weeks without a word. The "what if" fears swirled around in Mary's head. She couldn't sleep. Every day she stared at the map as if it held some answer as to where Pat might be. Even the children sensed that something was wrong. They became quiet and didn't ask questions about Daddy.

By the middle of the seventh week Mary was exhausted. That night, once all the children were asleep, she knew she had to get some rest. She went to bed and, for the first time in weeks, the fears did not win the battle with her fatigue and she fell into a deep, quiet sleep. But, suddenly, a loud pounding startled her awake. She jumped from the bed, ran to the children's rooms. They were all sleeping and the noise stopped.

I must have been dreaming, she thought, and turned back towards her room. The noise started again. She grabbed a robe and went to the top of the stairs. She took two steps, but then it was quiet.

She grabbed the rail. The pounding started again. It became louder and louder. She crept down each step filled with fear. By the time she reached the bottom step, she could tell someone was knocking on the door and heard a muffled voice calling, "Mary!"

She flung open the door and there stood Joe, the mailman, waving something in his hand. "Mary, I'm sorry if I woke you, but I've been working the night shift sorting mail, and look! Here's six letters from Pat. We think all this mail was held up because it came from the invasion of the Philippines. I didn't want you to wait another minute to get these letters."

Mary gasped her thanks to Joe. She clutched her letters, sat on the stairs, and stayed up the rest of the night reading each letter again and again. Some had parts censored out, but they all ended with "I love you."

When the war finally ended and Pat came home safely, he told only a few stories about his war experiences. He did like to show a photograph which had been in *Life Magazine*. It showed General MacArthur returning to the Philippines as he had promised. In the background, you can see some ships that were a part of this invasion. On one small ship, in the very corner, you can see the number 139—Pat's ship. Of course, Pat's whole family thought of him as a hero, right there next to General MacArthur.

Mary never talked much about how hard this war had also been on those at home, except when she told about the night Joe delivered her letters. "There were a lot of heroes in this war, but the one who was my special civilian hero was Joe, the mailman."

Mary and Pat were my parents. I was one of the little kids who slept through the night of the letters, and this has become our favorite war story.

Lâle Davidson

Photo by Emma Dodge Hanson

The Haunting of Zelda is based in part on a true story. The story was set in my Uncle Harrison's house near Pittsburgh which was torn down in the 1980s. My father's stone house, built by my ancestors right after the American Revolution, still stands in Allegheny County.

When I write and read, I'm drawn to quirky and fantastical literature where the unconscious world takes form and shape, and ideas walk, talk and breathe. My written stories have appeared in print journals: *The North American Review* and *Artists Unite* and online sites: *Eclectica Magazine*, *The Collagist* and *Gone Lawn*. My magical realist novel, *The Ciphery*, was a finalist for the James Fellowship, Heekin Group Foundation Award.

For ten years, I told stories as part of the Snickering Witches specializing in folktales about strong women. A professor of English, I have taught fiction writing, fantasy, composition, and public speaking at SUNY Adirondack in upstate New York since 1993. I perform solo on request.

Lâle Davidson
laledavidson.com
laledavidson@gmail.com

The Haunting of Zelda

Lâle Davidson

As I stared at the outhouse leaning at a precarious angle and the rusted hand pump by the kitchen door, I wondered why I had come to my uncle's house. My uncle had died not long ago, but since the funeral, my father had been unable to enter his brother's house. You see, he had grown up there with his brother and two sisters. So I had come to clean it out for sale, or perhaps settle there myself. I had put by some savings and was in no rush to look for a job more dismal than the one I had recently left.

Empty houses are usually still as death, but when I opened the front door, I was met with the distinct impression of voices recently hushed. And though the passage in the hallway was blocked by huge sheets of peeling wallpaper, it seemed as though someone had just passed from one door to another. The Victorian lace curtains, now yellow and crisp as old paper, trailed to one side as though someone had just been standing there looking out the window. I had been worried about being lonely in this isolated house, but now I felt less alone than in the apartment I had let go.

The house was bisected by a hall with the front door on one end and a back door on the other. I brushed cautiously past the wallpaper curls and tried to open the back door to get a breeze going. But the door was jammed. No key was in the lock, and pull though I might, I couldn't budge it. To the right of the back door was my uncle's study. When I pushed it open, I was met with heaps of old papers that had taken a lifetime to collect and would take a lifetime to sort.

My uncle had been a minister and horse lover, with wavy reddish-brown hair, blue eyes and a devilish grin, always ready with a laugh and a gruff hug, smelling of cologne that barely covered the horse scent. This study showed a side of him I had never seen. Over the tops of cardboard boxes, black with soot, hard eyes gleamed through the darkness. A black and white photograph of my grandmother hung from a porcelain knob. On the floor, under the cracked upright piano, I found a child's schoolroom slate. Scratched awkwardly in chalk upon it was the name Zelda. I sounded out the name, stretching the vowels, lingering on the "el." Ze-e-lll-da. It seemed a little odd at the time. I had never known anyone named Zelda—certainly no one in my family. And how had the chalk survived without being brushed off?

In the first few days, I wasn't fully aware of the effect the house had on me. At night the house whispered to itself, an ongoing hush-a-bye of creaking floorboards and shifting timbers, a soft-sighing recantation of long-dead secrets just below the threshold of hearing and just above the murmur of thought.

Many times during the first few weeks, I was pulled out of the refuge of sleep by the ruffled purr of the boiler igniting itself in the basement. But was it the boiler that woke me? Sometimes, I would lie there, listening to my own breath, and become frightened that the breath was not my own. Once, in the somber blues of dawn, beneath a mourning dove's coo, one sound distinguished itself from all the others: a light footfall outside my bedroom door.

By day, as I cleaned, I told myself that habit is a blind and powerful force that can keep things in motion long after the death of their source. Even inanimate objects contained a memory of sorts. The steps were used to being walked on, so they continued to creak, a quiet rasp, a dry snigger; the living room was used to being lived in, so it rustled; and the lights, used to being dimmed, so they winked on and off as if enjoying some private joke. But by night my dreams grew troubled. In them, windows flew open and slammed shut with a violence and fury I didn't know my mind could possess.

My cleaning grew more intent and almost obsessive. I found a key that fit the back door. I tried it, but it wouldn't turn the lock. I opened the windows of my uncle's study wide to air it out. But I couldn't stop myself from looking at the portrait of his mother— my grandmother. It became a bad habit, like picking a scab too soon—and too often. Even from other rooms, I felt my eyes straying back to the back door and the portrait in the study. I began to notice that on sunny days my grandmother's face looked stern, a fierce light shining in her eyes. But on cloudy days, when the study grew particularly dark, the dogmatism turned to desperation, and the stern lines looked more like those of suffering. I wondered what she had guarded and what she had lost. Had she felt the same sadness, the same disconnection from the busy world that I did? Was that where I got it from?

I thought I would ask my father, if he ever called. I had left several messages, but he wasn't good with answering machines.

As the days passed, I polished the old furniture to a living glow and swept the floors to worn cleanliness. And all the while a miscellany of noises followed me about the house, never very far away. It made me edgy but strangely comforted. I'd think they were just outside the door I was washing, but when I went into the kitchen to empty my cleaning bucket, it seemed that they came from under the kitchen table. It got so that I was constantly jumping and turning around with a pounding heart.

Then, as the leaves fell, I began to find and mislay things. I found a jump rope tied to a door handle. After a rainstorm, a red India rubber ball materialized in a mud puddle in the front lane. I found my comb in the refrigerator several times and my glasses hanging off a low branch. One evening, I was sitting before the fire doing crossword puzzles. I was sure someone tugged my hair. When I turned back to my puzzle, I couldn't find my pen anywhere. It felt almost like a game I might have played with my uncle when I was a child.

Winter came white and bitterly cold. The high blue dome of autumn sky collapsed into a flat slate. And whenever I stepped outside, the wind tore at my face. My grandmother's face suffered more. She looked drawn and haggard, her stiff back seemed to strain against the black poplin of her dress, the muscles around her eyes were frozen, and she gritted her teeth behind pressed lips, as if fighting to hold something back.

The little shuffling and tapping noises steadily grew louder and more violent. One day, a leg of my armchair suddenly collapsed, and the whole thing caved to one side. The mirror of my grandmother's marble-top dresser tilted back and slammed against the wall. One morning I was wounded to find my favorite bowl smashed on the kitchen floor. And what was worse, the bowl had been propelled with such force that the blue porcelain was now only colored sand. I found teeth marks on the arms of an old doll and my pillowcase shredded. And constantly, black, ice-coated branches clacked against the window like angry bones.

I began to wake in the morning exhausted by dreams, yet could only remember them as dark and heavy shapes which seemed to sit on me for the better part of the day.

Finally one morning I managed to rescue one image from my lost nightmares. It was the face of a little girl with large gray eyes and wavy blonde hair. She was running out in the snow with bare feet. Her dress trailed out of her half-buttoned coat. I called to her, but she would not come to me, she only turned and looked at me, her face pale with dark rings under her eyes. Her brow wrinkled in anger.

I brooded on her face all day long.

That night, as I sat in the living room with a blanket wrapped tightly around my legs for warmth, I could not concentrate on my reading. The wind whipped around the roof of the house, making high bottle notes on the lip of the chimney. No matter how much I stirred the fire with the poker, it seemed to suck the warmth out of the room. I kept seeing her small bare feet in the snow. But where were her shoes?

The tiny hairs stood up on the back of my neck. My blood squeezed painfully through my temples. I heard something. Something other than the wind.

"Mama!" A small, high voice called at the back door. "Let me in!"

It was Zelda and I knew it. What should I do? Let her in? I stood up and froze. What if she was evil? What if she wanted revenge? I picked up the poker. What could *I* do to help her?

The calling continued, so sad, so persistent. "Mama! Let me in."

Time tilted, stretched, and collapsed. I stopped breathing to hear her better. "Mama!"

The voice was so small, so shaken with cold. So surprised. Not angry at all.

I became speed itself. I wrenched at the door. But it was still jammed. I stabbed at the crack with a poker, thinking to lever it open. The crying went on and on, a voice that couldn't understand why it wasn't being heard. I thought the sound would kill me.

All at once I understood the expression on my grandmother's face. She had always heard that voice calling her, and her insides longed to go to it.

I ran outside and around the house to the back.

But there was only a small snowdrift that the wind had blown up against the door. And the wind had stopped.

The voice was gone.

I just stood there, empty.

If it would have helped, I would have taken the very snow into my arms. And perhaps it would have helped me. For I have never felt a loss like I did on that night.

The house was silent after that. Not a timber stirred. The silence was worse to me than all the frightening noises I had ever heard.

I recognized this silence. It was the silence of my father.

"Dad?" I finally got him. "Who was Zelda?"

There was a sudden absence at the end of the line, a tiny void. Then he said hazily, "Didn't I ever tell you about…?"

Zelda was his youngest sister. She was too young to go to school, so she stayed home while the others went. One winter day, their mother bundled Zelda up and sent her out to play in the snow, to get her out of her hair. My grandmother was a hard working woman and had a lot to do. She got so involved in some project that she completely forgot about Zelda. Hours passed. When she remembered, she ran outside in a panic. "Zelda?"

No one answered.

She followed Zelda's tiny footprints though the snow. They led all over, to a tree, a jump rope tied to the outhouse door, a red ball in the upper lane, and finally to the back door, where Zelda lay huddled in a tiny, freezing heap, crying for her mother to let her in. My grandmother hadn't heard her cries, and Zelda was too young to know that no one ever used that door.

Zelda took a chill that day, got pneumonia, and died. My grandmother took to her bed for a long time.

"How long?" I asked.

"I don't … know." I imagined my father and my uncle, two boys, standing in some silent eternity beside their mother's bed.

"She was convinced she was going to hell," he told me. "But it wasn't the idea of punishment that bothered her. It was the thought that if she went to hell, she would never see her baby girl again."

Finally, she had a dream. A man she believed was Christ hovered at the foot of her bed, his black eyes gleaming on either side of his hawkish nose, the toes of his bare feet splayed from so much walking. He held up two fingers of his right hand and said, "You are saved." She rose from her bed and went on with life.

But I wondered if my father ever truly had gone on with his.

The house stayed silent all through January and February. A long history of silence had saturated the woodwork, so heavy it dulled all fear and pain.

But the seasons changed, as they always do, and with the softening of the cold, the noises returned: first with a little knocking here, and a light tapping there. I could have cried with relief. Even as I recognized how strange it was to welcome a spirit of loss, I made a place for her at my table.

I relished the noises following me about. I laughed as I looked for things I knew I hadn't mislaid. I hugged the bitten doll in my arms. For the haunting of Zelda answered something in me that I had never known was a question.

Alden (Joe) Doolittle

Photo by Meredith Kaiser

Alden (Joe) Doolittle is known by audiences throughout upstate New York for his humorous and good-natured style of storytelling. He loves to tell personal and family stories as well as historically-based tales about the Hudson and Mohawk Valleys and the Erie Canal. He applies storytelling in his work as a healthcare consultant and volunteer chaplain at Albany Medical Center. Joe is co-producer of Story Circle at Proctors Theatre, a resident company offering programs including Story Sundays at the Glen Sanders Mansion, the annual Tellabration at Proctors and Story by Story on Public Access TV. In 2013 Joe was honored by the National Storytelling Network with the Oracle Award for Leadership and Service.

Alden (Joe) Doolittle
www.storycircleatproctors.org
aldenjoe@nycap.rr.com
518-384-1700

Families are treasure troves of material for a storyteller. With material so bountiful, and memories so rich, a teller has to be careful to discern whether the story meets the test of being entertaining, and perhaps educational. Does the story deal with a specific aspect of the teller's family and also help the readers and listeners generate and reflect on their own family stories.

The two stories that follow meet that test. They come from two points in Joe's life, separated by fifty years. They are echoes from that place in Joe's memory where comfort and solace rest, where he travels when he needs strength and support, and just to feel good. They are intended to be generative, to stimulate memories of the reader's family, to encourage harvesting of precious moments, traditions, and time together. They speak to the glue that holds families together: loving relationships and budding traditions.

Pop's Whisper

Alden (Joe) Doolittle

My father ("Pop") and I shared a first name, Alden. Only once can I recall addressing him that way.

As a kid, after homework and rationed TV, I'd settle into bed with my current favorite book. I'd read with one ear cocked for the sounds of my father's coming to bed: the closing refrigerator door, the creak of the first step of the hallway stair, the strong pace up the steps. Then I'd click off the light. Occasionally, my ears were fixed more on the story being told from the page and I'd miss those warnings until his hand turned my doorknob and his voice spoke roughly. "Turn off your light and go to sleep!" It was a loving admonishment and I'd duck under the covers.

One January night after 11:00 PM, I heard the squeak of the stairs. I clicked off my light and nestled in to wait for a flush of the toilet and sigh of his bedspring to continue reading.

My father's step paused at the top of the stairway. He turned and I heard the sound of his steps headed towards my door.

45

"Alden, are you awake? I heard your light click." His whisper came through my slightly opened door. "Come to the hall window, and don't turn on the light."

I stepped into the chill and then the half-light of the hall. God's neon was framed in the north-facing hall window. A greenish-gold-indigo filled the space. The Aurora Borealis! We stood together in awe.

He was a large man. I was 11 and stood only to his elbow. After precious silence, he spoke, again in a whisper, "We both have things to do tomorrow and should be in bed. It's spectacular, for sure, but …. Good Night, Alden."

"Good night, Alden," I replied looking up. I sensed a closeness that was always there, but rarely spoken. Returning to my room, I nestled into cold sheets, feeling the glow and holding the closeness.

Over the years the spirit and the memory are there whenever I need to hear them—a whispered "Good night, Alden."

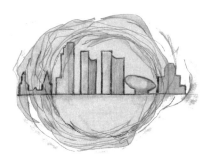

Traditions, Hands, Families and the Holy Spirit

Alden (Joe) Doolittle

What's a tradition? Something a group of people do because it's important to the way we live, as families, as communities, as nations. The root comes from the Latin, literally to "hand over."

This is a story of a new tradition at the Doolittle's.

My mother passed away in December 2009, a few days shy of her 105th Christmas birthday. We've always been challenged to observe her holiday birthday and make the celebrations fit together. After years of angst our family was "handed" a solution to this dilemma.

In 1994, just before Thanksgiving, I heard a friend describe a tradition he'd participated in at someone else's Thanksgiving. Everyone at the table traced his or her hand on the tablecloth. Later, the lady of the house stitched around each handprint, adding the person's name and the date. There was a tablecloth of "hands" for each holiday, updated each year with those attending and the date. It was a tapestry of holiday participation. The tablecloth had even outlived some of the family members, yet their hands were still around the table, sharing the holiday.

As I retold my wife Gay the story, she said, "Why don't we make one for your mother's birthday? She'll be 90! We've got a bunch coming for Thanksgiving, and the out-of-towners can send us a tracing and a greeting. I'll do the sewing." And so we selected a long, light blue tablecloth and colorful calico prints for the hands. Gay cut the calico from paper tracings of each hand.

About two weeks before Christmas, Gay called me into her sewing room. She was experimenting with a layout, a saddle of calico riding a wave of blue. She had left a space in the middle. "You know, it would be great if we could get your mother's hands right here in the middle. She should be present when we use it down the road."

"Great idea," I said. "But how am I going to get a tracing of her hands, without blowing the surprise?"

"That's not my problem," she retorted.

So a day later, I stopped by to visit my Mom at her assisted living apartment. I said I was doing a project with a Sunday school class and needed tracings of "old hands" to go with my younger students. She was pleased to participate. I traced her hands, we continued the visit and I returned home with my prize centerpiece. Including my mom's, there were 32 hands represented on the tablecloth.

That Christmas Day, after dinner at my brother's and a board game, we gathered for dessert. The table had been cleared and reset. The new tablecloth lay there, with its pattern of loving hands. Mom was quiet as she studied it, savoring the special care and love that had gone into making it.

"Oh how wonderful!" Mom finally exclaimed. "How did you get them all? And the calico print colors are beautiful. Oh thank you!" After a while, Mom looked up at Gay and said, "You did this beautiful piece for me, didn't you? I love it, and I love you."

"I love you too, Mom," Gay replied. In all my years of marriage, this was the only time I heard my wife and mother say they loved each other.

Mom's hands are in the middle of the tablecloth, connected by the phrase from the hymn, *Blessed Be the Tie that Binds*. She noticed the greetings near each hand print: "Happy Birthday to an incredible Grand Ma"; "Thank you for you guidance"; "Thank you for your fine example"; "Good Cheer, Love." And from one teenage great-grandchild, "Our family is crazy!"

Yes to be sure, we may be crazy, although who isn't at Christmas? Since that occasion, we've felt more connected as family across the miles. We use the tablecloth when family members visit, on Thanksgiving and Christmas or just about anytime. We've added hands at other gatherings, as the family has grown with new spouses and great-grandchildren. The tablecloth has outlived some of its hands, although they are all still present at the table. Our tradition of connection continues to be handed down through the generations.

The author, at far right, shares a view of the tablecloth of family hands with members of his audience, in Barneveld, New York.

Kate Dudding

Photo: The Daily Gazette

With a specialty in researching, composing and telling true stories of people who made a difference, I've told stories throughout the northeastern USA and won the Story Slam at the 2010 National Storytelling Conference in Los Angeles.

My first three CDs won national storytelling awards. My fourth, *Fighting For Our Rights: American Women Mid-20th Century,* released in 2014, contains stories of women fighting for civil and women's rights during a time when white women could not rent cars, be on juries in many states or get a mortgage. African American women faced even more obstacles.

Since 1999, I have produced over 150 storytelling events for adults with Alden (Joe) Doolittle. I was honored to receive the 2008 Northeast Region ORACLE Award for Leadership and Service from the National Storytelling Network.

Kate Dudding
www.katedudding.com
kate@katedudding.com

May your days be filled with stories!

Kate Dudding

The Story of
One American Soldier

Kate Dudding

I do solemnly swear
that I will support and defend the Constitution of the United States
against all enemies, foreign and domestic;
that I will bear true faith and allegiance to the same;
and that I will obey the orders of the President of the United States
and the orders of the officers appointed over me,
according to regulations and the Uniform Code of Military Justice.
So help me God.

Oath of Enlistment, United States Army

Every U.S. Army soldier solemnly swears this Oath when they enlist. This is the story of one American soldier.

His family moved to the United States in 1990 when he was eight. They all proudly became naturalized citizens eight years later. When he graduated from high school, he thought of joining the army. He told his family that he had skills that few native-born Americans have, skills he had learned in his birth country that would be useful to the U.S. Army. But instead, he went to college as his father wished.

Then, September 11th, 2001 happened. His sister later said, "September 11th had kind of made the decision for him." Four days after September 11th, he joined the U.S. Army Reserve and solemnly swore that oath.

His reserve unit was mobilized during the initial invasion of Iraq in 2003. Because of his name, this American soldier had to put up with comments from fellow soldiers: "What kind of last name is that?" "Are you sure you're fighting for the right side?"

On the telephone, his brother and sister asked, "Is it worth it, with everyone giving you so much mouth?"

He just said, "This is the only way I have to show that I love this country."

While in Iraq, he came under heavy mortar fire and had to sleep in his combat gear.

This American soldier, Mohsin Naqvi, returned home on leave after four months in Iraq to make a surprise visit in time to celebrate the end of Ramadan. For Muslims this is a time of great celebration, with families gathering together in the way other families gather together for Christmas or Passover. If family members can't come, they are called. Mohsin's family had been expecting only to speak with him over the telephone so, when he actually arrived home, they were joyous. His father said, "It is the best holiday of my life."

During his furlough, Mohsin told a local reporter, "It was scary at times. But I knew everyone in the community here was praying for me." He added, "It's still a little weird having running water."

"Mohsin is always cracking jokes," his family and friends said. "He is the kind of guy who could make a joke out of anything no matter how terrible the situation was. He is the life of the party."

Mohsin returned to Iraq and served a total of nine months there. After graduating from college, he re-enlisted for active duty, solemnly swearing that oath again, and he became a first lieutenant. "This is going to be my career," he told his family. "The only way I'm getting out of the army is if they kick me out, which isn't going to happen, or if I retire."

In June 2008, when he was 26, Mohsin married. Several days later, he left his 20-year-old bride and was deployed to Afghanistan, where he could use his special skills. Being a native of Pakistan and an Urdu speaker as well as a Muslim, he could communicate with Afghans and reassure them about American intentions.

Three months later, on Sept. 17, 2008, while on patrol in Afghanistan, 1st Lt. Mohsin Naqvi and three other American soldiers were killed by a roadside bomb. They were among the 155 U.S. soldiers who died in Afghanistan that year.

Mohsin was buried with full military honors at a solemn Muslim ceremony in Colonie, New York, 18 years after he moved to the United States, 10 years after he became a naturalized citizen.

Brigadier General Bill Phillips presented Mohsin's family with his Purple Heart, his Bronze Star, his Combat Infantry Badge and his dog tags. "Mohsin served his army with great distinction," he said. "He was a real patriot."

Mohsin's father said, "We are patriotic Americans. We are proud to be Americans...but still, people don't trust us. Why are we Muslims being blamed for something done by 19 people? Why? Why is that? We are patriotic Americans. My son did the best he could because he sacrificed his life. He's down there in that grave under tons of dirt. What else can you expect from a patriotic American?"

Mohsin's 18-year-old brother said, "Mohsin said he had to stay in the army because it was the only way he had as a Muslim to show he also loved this country. There is no one that I know who loved this country more. Mohsin is my hero, and I hope everybody else can look to him and say the same."

I first learned of Mohsin Naqvi by watching a video* of his funeral in a town near my home. Through the local Interfaith Story Circle of the Tri-City Area** I have become friends with Muslims and learned how they are sometimes treated very unfairly in our country. Being touched by Mohsin's sacrifice and saddened by the prejudiced treatment he received while in service to his beloved country, I wanted to tell his story. I learned that he grew up in Newburgh, NY, 100 miles south of my home, and was married and buried near his wife's home, a town that neighbors mine.

Mohsin Naqvi
Department of Defense via
Poughkeepsie Journal/AP

* www.timesunion.com/default/media/Funeral-of-1st-Lt-Mohsin-Naqvi-3017.php
** www.interfaithstory.org/tricity

New Memories of
Marilyn Monroe

Kate Dudding

I thought I knew everything about Marilyn Monroe, sex symbol and movie star of the 1950s and 60s. So I was surprised to read that Marilyn Monroe had changed Ella Fitzgerald's life by making a phone call.

It started in 1953. Marilyn was preparing for the film *Gentlemen Prefer Blondes*, her first musical. She was advised by her vocal coach: "Buy Ella Fitzgerald's recording of Gershwin songs and listen to it a hundred times."

Marilyn was not into jazz and she certainly hadn't heard of Ella Fitzgerald. Despite Ella's sweet, silvery voice and endlessly inventive vocal improvisations, she was not well known yet. But listening over and over to the record *Ella Sings Gershwin*, not only did Marilyn learn how to sing, she also became a fan. *Gentlemen Prefer Blondes* was a huge success.

Marilyn went on to star in several other smash hits including *The Seven Year Itch* (where she wore that white halter dress and stood on top of a subway grate to get cool one hot summer night). Marilyn also continued to buy and listen to records by Ella Fitzgerald.

Two years later in 1955, Marilyn just had to make that phone call. She was now 29 years old and a Hollywood superstar. Ella was 38 and, after 20 years of performing, was still singing in small, second rate jazz clubs—dingy places with sticky floors and rooms reeking of smoke and spilled beer.

It was 1955 when African Americans rarely sang in the first rate jazz clubs. In fact, when traveling they had difficulties finding hotels where they could stay and restaurants where they could eat. It was 1955 when Rosa Parks refused to give up her seat on a bus in Montgomery, Alabama. It was 1955 when 14-year-old

Emmett Till was brutally murdered in Mississippi for speaking to and, perhaps, whistling at a white woman.

It was 1955 when Marilyn, because of her deep admiration for Ella's artistry, decided to change Ella's life.

Marilyn called the owner of the Hollywood nightclub where Frank Sinatra made his Los Angeles debut in 1943.

Marilyn told the nightclub's owner, "I've never seen Ella Fitzgerald perform. I want you to book her for a week immediately."

"You know I can't. She's black."

"If you do, I will take a front table every night. The press will go wild."

"I'll do it."

Marilyn kept her word—she was there, at a front table, every night. The press went wild.

Ella Fitzgerald and Marilyn Monroe in the Mocambo Club, 1955

Ella went on to have a long career—singing in all the best venues.

She told many people, "I owe Marilyn Monroe a real debt. After my first week in Hollywood, I never had to play a small jazz club again. She was an unusual woman—a little ahead of her time."

However, Marilyn did NOT have a long career. After 1955, she made several movies, including my personal favorites, *Some Like It Hot* and *Bus Stop*.

In 1962 at age 36, Marilyn gave her last interview, just weeks before her death. Marilyn pleaded with the *Life Magazine* reporter: "Please don't make a joke of me. End the interview with what I believe."

He, or his editor, didn't quote Marilyn's beliefs. Instead, the article ended with Marilyn talking about fame: "If fame goes by, I've always known it was fickle. So at least it's something I experienced. But that's not where I live."

Here's how Marilyn wanted that article to end—here's what she believed: "What the world needs is a real feeling of kinship. Everybody: stars, laborers, Negroes, Jews, Arabs. We are all brothers."

I hadn't known that was what Marilyn believed.

Now I wonder what *else* I don't know about Marilyn Monroe.

Margaret French

Many of the personal stories I tell have their roots in Canada, the land where I grew up, or in upstate New York where I live now. They are often humorous, sometimes touching, occasionally quirky tales about our all-too-human condition. In a performance I often add some local history, favorite traditional folktales, or myths.

I perform throughout the Capital District and beyond, including in Word Plays and Tellabration at Proctors Theatre, Story Sunday at Glen Sanders, Caffè Lena, and many other venues.

I enjoy leading both writing and storytelling workshops. The stories people told in a recent series of workshops were recorded by staff at the Folklife Center at Crandall Library in Glens Falls and are available through their website.

Please visit my website and blog. If you'd like to have me tell stories or lead a workshop for your group, contact me anytime.

Margaret French
Saratoga Springs, New York
www.margaretfrench.com
margaretefrench@gmail.com
518-879-6451

Song for Sunday Mornings

Margaret French

I sit with her on Sunday mornings so her husband can go to church. For more than thirty years, they always went together. Often she would be asked to speak during the service.

"She was the smart one," he told me. Now he goes to church alone.

An RV rusts in the side yard. When she and her husband first learned of her future, they traveled 'round the country to make the most of whatever good time she had left.

Inside the house, old-fashioned crafts, cookbooks on a kitchen shelf and photos of her children tell me of the woman she used to be; photos of her grandchildren tell me of joys she can never experience.

She is too young—not much older than I—to be suffering from advanced Alzheimer's. She can't walk, can't even change position in her bed or recliner. She can't dress or feed herself. She can't speak. She's been this way for years.

Before I come, her husband bathes her, dresses her, feeds her and either props her up in a recliner or lays her back in the hospital bed in the living room. And when he goes, I sit in the chair beside her. I read or knit, recite poetry aloud or tell her stories.

Usually she ignores me. Sometimes she looks puzzled, as if to say, "Who are you and why are you here?" Sometimes she seems enraged and I stop whatever I'm doing at that moment or resume whatever it was I stopped. She never looks happy. She never smiles.

Sometimes I stroke her forehead and cheek. She may close her eyes. Sometimes she gets angry and I draw my hand away. Once, when I stopped, she drew the back of her hand to her cheek as if to stroke her face herself, but mostly she lies quietly, apparently indifferent. And she never smiles.

It is quiet. Her husband leaves the radio playing softly, oldies mostly. I don't think she pays attention. I have time to read the Sunday paper, catch up on unread books, knit without interruption.

One small detail about this routine is odd. Every week for all these months, I find myself singing to her, singing the same song, in French no less. Surely I would at least sing a song likely to stir some old memories in her ailing brain. But no, I sing a French-Canadian folksong that I learned decades ago in French class. Heaven knows my voice is off key. (When my children were little, they used to beg me not to sing.) Still I sing this old folksong every week. She looks my way, or ignores me or gets angry. If she looks angry, I stop.

"Ah, si mon moine voulait danser … un capuchon je lui donnerai …. Danse mon moine danse, tu n'entends pas la danse, Tu n'entends pas le moulin lon la, Tu n'entends pas le moulin marcher."

The words are simple: If my monk wanted to dance, I would give him a hood. Dance, my monk, dance. You don't hear the dance. You don't hear the mill. You don't hear the mill running.

It's just a light-hearted song about a girl tempting a monk to dance. Why would I sing it? I was puzzled.

One night I woke up, finally understanding. I have thought of myself as a bystander to a family's troubles. Little is asked of me. But I am not merely knitting the morning away so a husband can have a break. I am affected too. I ache for a woman unable to know either the pleasures of life, like the music of the dance, or the work of life, like the sound of the mill grinding grain for a village.

My song is an invitation, but not for her. I know she can never join the dance again. She can't even smile. I've been singing the song for myself. I have made a little card to carry with me as long as I have my wits about me. On it I've written the words *Hear the Dance*. And I try to remember to smile.

Locked into Teaching

Margaret French

I did it for the money, $1,500 for six weeks. (And to broaden my horizons and serve humanity.) Beatrice, my office mate at the college, has taught there for years, and she is probably no braver than I. Surely I could teach one summer course at the nearby maximum security prison for men.

Before the term began, the prison authorities had to put me in their system. Getting fingerprinted was fascinating, but messy. I got ink on the cuff of a white blouse that won't come off. I suppose my fingerprints are now in some national data bank. If I should ever do anything illegal, I'll be caught within hours, and my family humiliated. So I am really careful.

A correction officer took my picture and made two ID cards, one for me to carry inside the prison and one for their files, so they would know what I looked like if I never made it back from class. He reminded me to lock my car—always—before I came into the prison. (But who wouldn't?)

My colleagues had already given me advice about teaching in a prison.

"Dress conservatively," Beatrice reminded me. "It's an all-male prison." So I wore my usual white blouse, longish navy skirt, sensible shoes, one heel a little wobbly, but who really notices?

Roy had said, "You've got to keep discipline, or they won't do any work for you. You're too damned soft." Then he went on to tell me a long irrelevant story about a poisonous snake that lay half-frozen on the highway until some foolish, soft-hearted person nursed it back to health, and it bit her and she died. Roy added, "That person would be you."

The first day of class, the officer at the front desk compared my face to the one on my ID and waited while I locked my watch and purse in a locker. He checked my textbooks, attendance book, notes, handouts, pens, Kleenex, and the emergency chalk and markers I always carry in case none is in the classroom. He sent me through a metal detector and set me free to enter the prison, or rather, go through the first of three sets of heavy sliding metal bars.

The bars behind me slid shut and locked before the bars ahead of me began to open. For a little while I was trapped between them. If there were a prison riot, I would be safe, I guess, sort of, locked between the bars. After the third set of bars, there I was, at one end of a very, very, very long hallway. You would expect a correction officer to walk with me to keep me safe. But no, I had to walk to my classroom. Alone. I was glad I was wearing conservative clothing, for the men all seemed to be looking at me as I walked past them.

I stopped to get talked to by the education officer. "Whatever you do, don't criticize the men during class. They won't tolerate being put down in front of their peers. Woman or not, they'll take you out." He added, "If you have any problems, call out; I'm just down the hall." Not in the classroom, but *somewhere* down the hall. I haven't screamed in any serious way in my entire life, so I earnestly hoped that nothing went wrong.

It was almost time for class. I adjusted my pile of books and papers a little, put my head down and scurried towards the classroom, preoccupied, wondering how I was supposed to keep discipline at all costs while never criticizing anybody. The door was open. I noticed the rows of men sitting at metal desks waiting for me, but not the step up into the room.

My wobbly heel caught on the sill, and I was flat on my face on the floor—books, papers, pens, Kleenex, emergency chalk and markers scattered around my outstretched arms and legs. Silence. I kept my eyes down, picked up my belongings, dumped everything on the battered metal teacher's desk and sat down. More silence. I looked up at twenty-five big silent men. Most had huge necks, chests, biceps—the result of long sentences to lift weights. They didn't smile or move; they looked at me and waited.

"Good morning." My voice was squeakier than usual. "Today we begin Introduction to Literature. We'll be studying poetry, short stories, and *Hamlet*." And I continued to stumble through my first class.

Weeks passed. They did the reading and spoke up in class, unlike most of my students at the college. We read parts of *Hamlet* out loud. I got to be both Ophelia and Gertrude. They said I wasn't bad. I got permission from the college to loan them a videotape of the play, and they watched it at night, which, they said, made it easier to learn. But they still didn't like Shakespeare and said so, often. I didn't criticize anyone in class, and no one beat me up.

I had one incident. One day, Tony made fun of another man for asking too many dumb questions. Quiet George, a gigantic man with biceps bigger than my waist, rose to his feet and bellowed, "Who are you, *?*#!?!, to tell him he can't talk in class?" And he jerked his head towards the door. They left abruptly, Tony first, George following.

I'll never see little Tony again, I thought.

Probably I should have done something. But I didn't have a clue what that something was. So I finished teaching the poem that begins *I wandered lonely as a cloud*…. You know, the one by Wordsworth about daffodils. After a while, George came back alone. I hoped Tony was alive and not badly hurt. The next day, Tony came back too. Nobody explained anything to me. And I didn't ask.

The men wrote papers, often pretty well, except for a few cases of *egregious* plagiarism. One student handed in a paper identical to one that another had handed in the week before. Back at the college, I expressed my disappointment to Roy.

"Margaret," Roy said dryly, "they're in prison for reasons more serious than plagiarism."

On the last day of class, we finished early. The men and I were almost comfortable together by then. They wanted to chat.

"Do you remember the time George took Tony out of class," one asked. I nodded. "We were all watching your face. If you had cried, none of us would have come back." Several agreed.

"And do you remember the first day of class? The day you fell on your face?" I doubted that I could ever forget. "We all thought it was the funniest thing we'd ever seen. The education officer came to talk to us afterwards."

"Men, I don't care how bad a teacher she is. You had no business throwing her on the floor like that."

Everyone roared with laughter but me. Class ended, and we said our good-byes. One student offered to carry my books down the long hallway.

Near the exit, a man I'd never noticed before sidled up to me and offered to carry my books outside to my car. (I really don't think it's allowed.)

"It's the red Dodge Colt," he said. "I watch you every time you leave."

And with this unsettling tidbit in mind, I walked alone from the prison to my rusty little red car. Summer was over, and so was my prison teaching career.

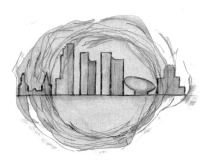

Marni Gillard

Photo by Kate Hannon
www.katehannon.com

Marni Gillard's Irish grandfather taught her to sing expressively by repeating, "Tell the story. Tell the story!" Those words soon directed her life's work. *Storyteller, Storyteacher* traces the transformation story-sharing brought to her middle school classroom and her life. Now in e-format, it's a must-read for educators helping youth discover their voices through writing and expressive speech. Marni witnessed how character, confidence, and community grow when learners *enter* and *speak from* a story's world. Her double CD, *Without a Splash: Diving into Childhood Memories,* shows how life tales become our teachers. Marni's work with interfaith tellers[*] breaks the barriers of difference. Her retreats, school workshops and Story Studio classes change lives. At Pyramid Lake's Storytelling Camp[**] in the Adirondack Mountains, Marni welcomes beginning and experienced tellers of every age.

[*] www.childrenatthewell.org
[**] www.pyramidlife.org

Marni Gillard
marnigillard@earthlink.net
www.marnigillard.com

One Toe In

Marni Gillard

A song surfaced in me years ago requesting a told tale. Returning now as writer helped me re-envision Maisie's world. I am grateful for Johanna Shogan's help and coach Doug Lipman's question about what Maisie found in the sea. Her discovery is akin to the song that once entered me. May your explorations of our treasury of tales guide you to songs and tales of your own.

Maisie lived within smelling distance of the sea. On summer days she raised her bedroom window to gulp its salty air. On windy nights, the sea's lapping soothed her like a mother's lullaby. She imagined tall waves beckoning, offering piggy-back rides. But she couldn't run to meet them. At nine years old Maisie had never climbed the wooden walkway over the dunes to the sea. She wasn't allowed.

Grandma, plump in her wheelchair, heard Maisie's pleadings but said, "Oh my dear, that sea could swallow you up! How I wish I could take you over the dunes and watch you play." Grandma's eyes looked sad, but they held some untold secret as well.

In contrast to Grandma, Maisie's Great-aunt Florence could speed-walk the beachside neighborhood with long striding legs twice most summer days. Maggie and Grandma marveled at Florence managing the heavy wheelchair safely down the back ramp and back up again after time in the yard. Gardening allowed the two elderly sisters and their young charge to enjoy hours in the sun and shade savoring the sea air together. Occasionally, Maggie's yearning for the sea would break their spell of contentment. "Please!" she'd whine. Then, "Why not?"

Aunt Florence's scowl inevitably ended the discussion. "That's enough now. Case closed."

Maisie's school chums included her in winter activities, but come summer, neighbors young and old headed over the dunes or to camps or to other vacation spots. Their invitations to Maisie were declined.

Her questions and imaginings grew as strong as Aunt Florence's long legs.

Florence's family had long ago built the elegant sandbox in a back corner of the garden. It boasted padded wooden seats and a slanted roof which kept Maisie's sand sculptures, cakes and imaginary friends fairly dry even on rainy days. She pretended her sea creatures, shaped with antique tin cookie-cutters, could talk to the sand people she created with her hands. They looked like a gingerbread family. Sometimes Maisie fantasized a real child to play with, someone who had enjoyed this same box and its toys long ago. Unable to picture Aunt Florence as a child, she figured it was a boy.

To her fantasy play Maisie lured worldly princesses. Their accompanying handmaids seemed polite enough, but as the princesses napped, the sassy servants planned mischief. One day, with the handmaids' encouragement, Maisie dared to climb the ramp and interrupt Grandma's and Florence's soap operas. She demanded knowledge. "Grandma, where is my *mother*? And shouldn't I have a *father* as well?"

The elderly sisters, startled, exchanged a look.

"Well…" Grandma began, looking toward her sister. "Perhaps it is time you knew *something* ."

Florence stood to speak. Looking straight at Maisie, she said, "If you must know, your father lived here as a boy. You play with some of his things. His trucks and soldiers are boxed away. Would you like to play with them as well?" She spoke the facts devoid of emotion.

"My *father*?" Maisie whispered as her heart raced.

"Yes," said her aunt whose voice grew even more stern. "His things are here, but he is not. Your grandmother and I have cared for you since he left you here as a baby. Case closed."

As the conversation ended, the sea roared.

Maisie left the room to rejoin the bold handmaids. She said to herself, "You say the case is closed, but just maybe it's finally *open*."

The garden and the girl both grew like weeds as summer passed. One day, while Aunt Florence went walking, Maisie dead-headed a row of daylilies under Grandma's watchful eye. Finishing, she asked, "Grandma, with my chore money, could I walk to the corner store for ice cream? I could bring a pint for us to share."

"Oh, that's lovely, dear," Grandma said. "Come straight home so it won't melt."

Maisie inspected each cottage as she walked, noticing sea decor and garden treasures. At a corner she overheard some ladies talking of a neighborhood tea party. As if dealing with her princesses, she politely interrupted. "Excuse me, did I hear you mention a tea party? My grandma and great-aunt *love* tea parties. Might they be included?"

The women smiled at the little girl and most nodded to each other. One, clearly worried about the wheelchair, spoke up. "Honey, we would love to have them join us, but *could* they come?"

"Oh, yes!" Maisie assured them. "My Great-aunt Florence rolls Grandma down the ramp and pushes her along the sidewalk. Could the tea tables be set up in a yard or empty garage in case of rain?"

The women seem pleased, as if they'd imagined that themselves. One promised, "I'll make the prettiest invitations and mail them each one tomorrow." Maisie was beyond pleased. She could jump for joy.

The day of the party the two elderly sisters powdered and rouged as if headed for a ball! Maisie promised she would weed a little and be happy in the sandbox for hours. As Aunt Florence guided Grandma's chair down the lane, the little girl waved and waved. She breathed the salty air in and out. Then she dashed toward the land of mystery beyond the dunes.

At the crest of the hill Maisie gazed at the waves she'd seen only in photos and on TV. The sea was a being, calling to her. Leaping white caps, like arms, reached for her. She marveled at the diamond-specked white sand so unlike her chocolate-colored box sand. She watched tiny-legged birds tease the tidewater till it turned and sent them scurrying. Her whole body laughed.

Removing her flip-flops she ran barefoot across the warm sand till a wide patch of beach adopted her. She wriggled her bum into its warmth. Marveling at the expanse of water and sand, she saw no houses, no gardens and no over-protective elders.

Maisie simply gazed out to sea. Owning a feeling of freedom, she noticed some music. A raggedy but happy-looking fellow was fiddling his way down the beach. His jaunty step made her giggle. He drew nods from onlookers but kept moving along. Maisie made sounds to go with his tune.

Dum dum dum da da dum dum da da.
Dum dum dum da da dum dum dum
Dum dum dum da da da da da da da da
Dum dum dum da da dum   dum   dum.

The tune slowed at the end of a passage then picked up as it began again. The fiddler, hearing the little girl, smiled at her and then glanced out to sea. Her relaxed and open mind spoke into the wind, *From the sea, now back to me!*

As if hearing her wish, the fiddler turned and pointed his bow directly at Maisie then back toward the water, as if inviting her to give the sea a try! Dressed in a suit both shabby and dapper, he looked to the girl like a handsome hobo. She laughed and said to herself, *He's fiddling for me!* She could sit still no longer. Dancing a jig toward the shore, she was caught in something that felt like magic.

The fiddler met her where her feet hugged the shore. He didn't speak, but with a mysterious smile began to sing the tune's words.

One toe in, and your soul will follow.
One toe in, and your heart will leap.
One toe in, if your spirit will allow you.
One toe in, and yourself   you'll   keep.

He sang the last words slowly, just as he had played them. He looked out to sea once more then down at the girl.

She met his gaze then turned to look out to the sea as well. Did she hear it whispering, "It's time?"

The fiddler's deep green eyes caught hers again, challenging her, but not frightening this girl kept from the sea. *Something* in his face looked like Grandma's when she marveled at the garden's beauty.

Maisie's words surprised even her. "Can I sing this song for *me?*"

The fiddler nodded.

"One toe in," she stopped for a breath, "and my soul will follow."

"One toe in," she put five toes in, "and my heart will leap."

"One toe in," she landed hard on, "*if* my spirit will allow me."

On the last line they sang in unison. "One toe in, and myself I'll keep."

Nodding with finality, like Aunt Florence after a job well done, the fiddler smiled then pointed toward the sea as if showing her something. The sun sinking made her squint. Was it a boat?

A wave suddenly drenched her feet, ankles and calves! Shivering and laughing, she accepted the invitation and stepped forward. The water now tickled her thighs. Remembering an idea, she dipped her hand, touched it to her lips and laughed. "Salty!" she announced to the gulls.

Maisie turned to look for the fiddler, but he was already backing down the beach, his task accomplished. He waved, smiling, and pointed his bow toward the horizon again.

She looked toward the water, marveling at the descending orange ball now striped by clouds of pink.

She looked back toward the fiddler once more but, still pointing his bow, he'd walked further away. She accepted his departure and gazed at what was no boat! A large sea turtle swimming toward her began singing in a watery voice.

One toe in, and your soul will follow.
One toe in, and your heart will leap.
One toe in, if your spirit will allow you.
One toe in, and yourself   you'll   keep.

Maisie could not stop laughing. The salty water splashed her face as he came closer. She had to sing along now, how could she

71

not? In her chest she felt the truth of the words. Her soul, heart and spirit were leaping and dancing and pulling her into this dream of a day.

"Climb on," the turtle instructed in his watery voice, half turning so she could. "Lay your chest against me. Just hold on. Sing, and 'yourself you'll keep.'"

Maisie hugged the turtle's wide back, cupping her fingers over his shell. They traveled straight out for a while then dove deep. A shock flowed through her. Yet somehow everything in her was sea creature too. Her hair flowed in the water. Her legs, dangling out beyond the shell, kicked. She held tight, enjoying the ride.

Sea beings of every size and color passed the girl atop the turtle. Some whizzed. Others slowed to stare.

"You knew it was time, and the fiddler guided you," the turtle's deep voice surprised her. "Now she's waiting too. We've all been waiting so long."

"Waiting for *me*? Someone is waiting?" Could it be true? The sea, calling her so long, had come for *her*?

"Oh, yes," Turtle answered.

Whole schools of fish and other lumbering swimmers, all singing Maisie's song, began to harmonize: "One toe in …"

Others whispered or called in fishy voices, "She's coming!"

A coral castle with open archways came into view. Maisie knew the sun above the sea had long ago set, but this mysterious undersea world had a light of its own. Turtle brought her to the castle's entrance. A beautiful woman stood smiling and waiting. Her deep, kind eyes met the little girl's. This was the *She* mentioned by Turtle. Her smile drew Maisie just as the ocean and fiddler had drawn her.

Maisie climbed down, setting her feet on the ocean's wet but sturdy bottom. Easily she accepted her mother's embrace.

Who else could it be? Neither said a word, but each recognized something familiar in the other's face. Maisie had dared ask for a mother only once. Now she knew that all along a mother's love had been here waiting for her to come *home*.

The coral castle offered unlimited time to hear stories of her parents' love and her own beginning.

"Your father's fiddling reached me all the way down here. His yearning pulled at my heart," her mother laughed, remembering. "Turtle's great-grandmother swam me up to his world. She sang to me as Turtle did to you. I took your father's hand and he helped me step out of the sea. Soon—we made you!"

Her mother's words seemed magical like the fiddler's tune. They brought the image of Maisie's father, that fiddler, to mind. How had he known when to meet her, she wondered. How had he fiddled her into the ocean as he'd fiddled her mother up from its depth? Maisie pictured them young and in love, holding her.

"His music lured me to his world, but it couldn't keep me there, even for you, my darling girl. The sea was my home. I assumed he couldn't come here, but now you have. I don't think settling in any one place would have made him happy. How he won me, I still don't know, but he did. We were young and confused, but we loved each other and we so loved you! His mother—your grandma—decided for us. She and that tall, no-nonsense sister of hers."

"Aunt Florence!"

"Oh yes," her mother laughed. "I remember Florence. Those two women settled it. They agreed to take you and keep you safe till your father and I learned to care for you. He promised he'd help you someday come to me, if the fates allowed. And here you are." Tears streamed down both their faces.

Maisie savored her sea life, its other-worldly sense of time, its shadowy light. She told her mother and closest sea-friends all about her life by the dunes. She acted out the sandbox dramas of the bold handmaids and polite, if spoiled, princesses. She described the colors and shapes of flowers from her garden, admitting she often felt lonely there, but knew she was loved and protected.

Her mother loved listening to Maisie's imitation of the bold handmaids. "Your imagination created these friends who helped you find the courage to escape the yard," her mother offered. "The servants and elegant princesses are as much a part of you as Grandma and Florence, and now me."

73

"They were so happy being invited and getting all dressed up! I'll remember them that way," Maisie said, sighing. "Do you think they *allowed* me to leave so I could find you?"

Maisie's mother's smiled. "They always knew you might go. They would not have stayed so close to the sea if they meant to keep you forever. Perhaps deep down they trusted you would know the moment, and you did!"

Time, like light, was different under the sea. Sleep always claimed Maisie after a long time playing and swimming with the friends she made. Turtle sometimes let her rest on his back as she had on her journey to the ocean's bottom. Most times they swam side by side exploring the sea's sunken treasures and its beauty. She and Turtle shared what they knew as well as their imaginary tales of land, sea and sky.

As Maisie grew, two places now were *home*. Her childhood sandbox, the garden, the house near the dunes was her first home. As time passed she began to feel a pull to return to it. She wanted to share all she had learned in her undersea home.

Shyly, one day, Maisie voiced her yearning, and her mother smiled. "Just as you sensed the right day to come here, you'll know when it's time to go. Just as you discovered mysteries here, you will find surprises in your first world. It has changed.

"You may be drawn to love, as I was. Maybe have a child of your own or children galore." Maisie pictured children happily digging in the sand and walking boldly into the sea. "Whether you return to me on your own or present me with a school of fish," her mother teased, "this home will always be yours." Maisie hugged her, feeling the truth of her mother's words.

The ache to return grew strong. Something was calling, pulling her back to the land, to the sky's clear light, to the salty air. Turtle, aging now too, appeared in time to taxi her to the sea's surface. Maisie's legs and arms had grown, but her center fit perfectly on his back.

"Just sing your song again," her mother whispered as they kissed good-by. "Singing brought you to my world. It will help you return to yours."

Maisie and Turtle waved and a procession of sea life accompanied them for a time. Finally, surfacing, she gulped the warm air and noticed the wind lifting the waves and swaying the trees. She heard familiar bird sounds and saw lights in windowed houses beyond the beach. Turtle got her singing as they moved toward shore.

One toe out, and my soul will follow.
One toe out, and my heart will leap.
One toe out - Yes! - my spirit will allow me.
One toe out, and myself   I'll   keep.

Gazing at the shore, Maisie spotted the fiddler. How did he know the exact day again? His now-silvery hair was long, tossed by the breeze. His smile, the same. But he wasn't playing. She saw the fiddle, silent, tucked into the pack at his side.

Maisie hugged Turtle's shell a final time, kissed the top of his head, and without a word pushed off toward shore. Swimming hard she imagined her father's music raising her beautiful mother from the sea. She recalled how his playful tune got her dancing down the beach and walking into its depths. Now *he* needs the music, Maisie thought. A tune or song to help him find his way to a long-ago love.

When Maisie stepped out of the sea onto warm dry sand, she became aware of her own wet clothes and skin. Her father's tender gaze took her in from head to toe. He lifted a huge soft towel and wrapped it about her. They both held tight till they needed to see each other's faces again.

In that embrace she'd heard an unknown music capable of sending a man into a deep and watery world. Maybe a daughter, now held by the man, could pull that music from him or make it herself. It could be as simple as putting one toe into the sea.

Jeannine Laverty

Jeannine Laverty has been telling international folk tales since 1979 when her work teaching English as a Second Language to immigrants in New York City showed her firsthand how the U.S. is made up of cultures of all the countries of the world.

Her school and museum performances and workshops for children have been awarded funding from the New York State Council on the Arts, the New York Foundation for the Arts and the National Institute for the Humanities.

For adults, Jeannine has taught weekend and week-long workshops in storytelling at Sagamore Conference Center and other Adirondack sites since 1980. She is part of the storytelling ensemble, SweetLand Storytellers, known especially for its program, "Voices from the Vietnam War."

In recognition of her long-term commitment to the art of storytelling, she was awarded the 1999 Northeast Region Award for Leadership from the National Storytelling Network.

Jeannine Laverty
Saratoga Springs, New York
jlaverty@nycap.rr.com
518-587-8932

Swallows

Jeannine Laverty

This story is dedicated to Laird Christensen. He lured me into the Masters of Science in Environmental Studies Program at Green Mountain College. He taught my first class as part of that program, Bioregional Theory and Practice, which should be required as a first class for every GMC student because it rids the mind of arbitrary state or county boundaries and fosters an understanding of land according to such natural qualities as watersheds, elevation, flora and fauna. I took so long to finish the degree that I also was able to take a newly developed class, Field Journaling, from Laird. There I studied the history and methods of recording natural-world observations. It was my last class in the program, which engendered this story. Laird's teaching was my alpha and omega.

Most of my classmates in Field Journaling chose a wilderness spot as their observation post, but I chose Denison Farm, from whose organically managed land I have eaten the main part of my diet for more than 20 years.

I started out as a Community Supported Agriculture (CSA) member when Janet Britt ran the farm, but since 2006, I've been a field worker for the current owners, Justine and Brian Denison. I thought I knew the farm and its surrounding hills pretty well, but I made many more discoveries when I took a quiet seat here and there on the farm to listen, watch, take notes and draw.

I always knew that the faster and more experienced workers could observe and work at the same time. But when I was not harvesting or weeding but attending, I saw the farm more fully. I noticed the pattern that Brian used to arrange the planting of the crops. I sketched the early morning spider webs and absorbed as I drew it the beautiful structure of the velvet leaf weed (which in Iowa we called butterprint). I struggled to capture, with my limited remembrance of perspective drawing, the jagged parts of the potato field that flooded out in the huge rains. I tried to capture the right colors and shading for my sketches of the blight that hit the potatoes and the tomatoes later in the season.

My fellow workers showed me things I would otherwise have missed. Fidelia pointed out the caterpillar of the giant swallowtail butterfly one day when we were doing our favorite job together—weeding the young carrots as the sun sank behind the trees. She didn't know the name of the butterfly, but she said, "It loves the parsley too, and the fennel, all the plants with the frothy leaves." When I looked up the caterpillar and its habitat, she was right, of course. What did it matter that she didn't know its name?

Errol and Walter, the two Jamaicans who live on the farm in the summer and return to their island in the winter, got involved in my project. They saw me fighting mosquitoes and frustration one humid afternoon of the week Laird wanted us to observe birds. It was after work for me, but Walter and Errol always work longer than the rest of us. They want to clock as many hours as possible in their five months here. They were coming back from picking zucchini, often their last job each day, and found me sweating and scratching beside the road from the Upper Field to the river ford. They work hard and fast, but they also take in every little bit of pleasure and learning available to them. Walter braked the rattling old farm-only van with its fading SoHo art gallery ID on the side. Errol jumped out, looked through my binoculars, quickly learned how to orient himself with my compass, noted my big journaling notebook and colored pencils, ran back around the van and jumped in just as Walter floored it and they roared off.

The next morning as we all assembled in the barn for our assignments, Walter said, "If you want to see the birds, you need to sit by the greenhouses in the Little Field. That's where they are every day that time." I knew he knew the farm and its happenings much more intimately than I did.

So after the morning's labor and lunch, I put the journaling supplies Errol had inventoried the day before and my folding camp stool in the van with the hoes and totes. After we weeded carrots and picked green beans and zucchini, I bailed out as we headed toward the barn at quitting time. I planned to set my stool in the wetland between the Little Field and the barn—and hope for birds. As I loped toward the middle of the soggy meadow, Errol yelled after me, "Jeannine, the bugs are gonna eat you alive!" But no! The birds were eating the bugs alive! How very satisfying!!!

The goldenrod towered over my head when I sat down. Above, swallows, 20 or 30 of them, swirled in continuous counterclockwise circles. They didn't stop dipping and gliding for at least half an hour. Never landing, they flew in curves that swung from high over my head to just skimming the goldenrod and me. Over the cattails they swooped, out across the melons and sweet potatoes, and back again. Below the swallows, dragonflies of all sizes and colors buzzed in straight, serious lines and angles, heading east, then northwest. It was Joy versus Patrol.

Meanwhile, in the ground-bound world of the goldenrod, bees and green flies toiled and buzzed in the blossoms, the bees' songs calm and continuous, the flies' frantic and intermittent. With those familiar sounds as background, I turned my attention downward into the matted undergrowth. There I saw many small, maybe 3/4", flying creatures occupying the airspace four to eight inches above the ground. They too were exploring the goldenrod, but never its flowers, as if hoping the bees and flies, or maybe especially the birds, wouldn't notice them at all. For a long time, all I could see was a flutter of rusty, mustardy-colored wings, a flight less focused than the feeders above them. I wondered if they were meat-eaters, finding among the leaves and stems some meal I couldn't see. The longer I sat, the closer they came, and the longer I watched, the more familiar their meandering flight became. Finally my brain found a match, having searched all the way back to the summer darkness in the Iowa yard of my childhood—these couldn't be lightning bugs, could they? They sure moved like them.

Eventually they were close and slow enough that I could see clearly—even without the hand lens Laird had assigned—their striped underbellies, the butterscotch brown of two outer wings that closed in a straight seam down the center of their backs. A perfect black rectangle marked the end of each wing. Imagine my pleasure when later at home, my Peterson's *Field Guide to Insects* printed on the color-plate page of the *Coleoptera* the soldier beetle! A brief description began with, "Similar to lightning bugs but…" That reward for my sustained observation made all the mosquito bites of the previous day worthwhile.

I can pinpoint the earlier moment when I began to give all the small and microscopic creatures their due. It has everything to do with why I came to Green Mountain College. Ten years ago in Cuba, I was visiting an organic citrus and cacao farm. We stood in the shade of the cacao trees, the leaf litter at our feet being turned and scratched by chickens. "We" comprised a bunch of Americans on the first Cuban organic-farms trip Global Exchange had offered and our hosts that day--local Communist party officials and an agronomist from the Universidad de Santiago de Cuba. As the officials smirked and rolled their eyes, the agronomist rhapsodized about the millions of microscopic lives under our feet and how it was this life that made everything else possible. As he described the myriad interactions of digestive and decaying processes, locating a number of them in our own bodies lest we miss his delighted point, I envied the chickens their meals, their usefulness, and their intimate if unconscious knowledge of their place in this system.

I respond dutifully to the Sierra Club's pleas to communicate with my legislators about polar bears, wolves and the Arctic Wildlife Refuge's caribou—the so-called charismatic fauna. But I'll know humans are really making progress when we cough up the money to rescue wildlife whose value we're just beginning to notice: swallowtail caterpillars, swallows, soldier beetles and all the tiny critters they eat. My afternoon of watching in the wetland proved to me that these small and seemingly abundant beings can be plenty charismatic. And they are crucial.

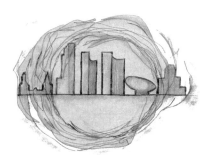

Bonnie Mion

Since I was five years old, I have danced. For years, I taught and performed hula and belly dance. I loved the exquisite beauty of both art forms, but hula had something belly dance didn't—it told a story. This delighted me so I began choreographing pieces based on the stories from the Middle East and Ancient Egypt.

I joined the Capital District Story Circle group and told stories without music, at the same time exploring my own family heritage. The fascinating personalities and the incredible events of their lives filled my days.

I now tell stories of harrowing and courageous escapades that show the power of persistence; the ingeniousness of creative problem solving; and the mysteries of life. All of my tales are interwoven with movement to enliven and enrich their expression. My greatest hope is that they are an inspiration to others, or at least a small bubble of joy, as we travel this journey we call life.

Bonnie's presentations are engrossing, breathtaking and beautiful. She is utterly charming, graceful and fascinating. ~ T.G.

Bonnie Mion
New Baltimore, New York
bjmion@gmail.com
518-756-8091

Nathaniel Schmidt
Adventures at the Dead Sea

Bonnie Mion

My grandmother, Dagmar Schmidt, told us this remarkable tale about my great grandfather, Nathaniel Schmidt, when we were growing up. It was a fascinating adventure, but there were so many missing details, which had always bothered me. I vowed that someday, when I was older, I would find out the whole story and get my answers. I began that investigation in 2011.

Researching the events of that fateful episode and learning about my great grandfather consumed my life for the next three years. After hundreds of hours of reading reports, letters, articles, books and archival material throughout the country, I finally was able to pull all the facts together. And it was worth it, because the tale was far more interesting than my grandmother had ever known!

This is based on the true story of the trip my great grandfather, Nathaniel Schmidt, took. He was a professor of Semitic Languages and Literature at Cornell University and the three students who traveled with him were Jesse Wrench and his cousin, Albert Olmstead, and Benson Charles.

I've created this version as though Jesse Wrench was giving a talk about the trip, twenty years after that cold day in February 27, 1905.

I still remember when the notary public signed it at his office. I watched the ink dry as I looked at the year, 1904. My passport was ready. *We are really going!* I thought. Then I clapped my cousin, Olmstead, on the back. He was so thin, unlike me. I could feel his ribs poking through his shirt. This was because he studied day and night and didn't eat enough. But he was the only one who was awarded a fellowship to go on this trip, whereas Charles and I had to pay our own way.

"How strange it will be not to go back to Ithaca this fall!" I said to Olmstead and our friend, Charles, as we walked down the street together. Charles, like Olmstead, was a bit taller than I was, and a bit more handsome. The girls giggled as he walked by, not at me though, unless I pinched them.

"Who cares about graduating this year anyway?" I leapt up on a nearby bench so I could tower over both my friends. "We get to study in Syria! Archeology! Original research! Entomology—Arabic cuss words! Beer made in the Holy Land!"

The bench toppled over and I crashed into Olmstead. He straightened his jacket and smirked over his wire-rimmed glasses. Charles simply picked up the bench and said, "Maybe you will learn something about how gravity works in Jerusalem too!"

They were used to me. My traveling companions were both twenty-four years old and I was only twenty-two so they treated me like a younger kid brother. At least I had a full beard whereas they didn't, so we looked the same age, more or less. They were as thrilled as I was; they just didn't show it as much.

Professor Schmidt was as excited as we all were to see the places of the Bible. It was the dream of a lifetime. After all, he was also a Baptist minister. And he looked the part with his neatly trimmed brown beard and mustache. He had a sturdy shorter build like me, but a powerful presence nonetheless. Schmidt had that self-assured air of confidence and poise that could captivate and enthrall a crowd wherever he went, whether it was Carnegie Hall, an international convention or a freshmen fraternity house. His classes at Cornell were so popular, students from many other disciplines audited them. They sat in the aisles, on the window sills and stood in the back of the room to hear his lectures.

The "Prof," as we called him, was an expert in the Bible, ancient history, Egypt, and the Near East. Many people said he knew fifty languages, which didn't count all the dialects he was also fluent in. He had an outstanding gift for oration. One night he gave a talk to a group of very rowdy fraternity boys. The school administration had asked him to

Nathaniel Schmidt circa 1906

84

befriend this difficult group of young men who were involved in hazing and other such unruly behavior. They were hoping the Prof would be a good influence.

Apparently he was, because those forty-five bulky athletes, who were not known for their love of scholastics, were entranced for over six hours and even skipped their dinners to hear him talk about ancient history! The Prof had a well-earned reputation on campus. As you can imagine, when other students heard we were given the opportunity to travel a whole year with Professor Schmidt, they were more than a little jealous.

On the other hand, sometimes you couldn't get the Prof to stop lecturing. We knew that too. I think he would have given a speech to a rock if he thought it would listen. And he would have told it how it could be a more ethical block of mineral and how historians are indebted to the contribution that rocks have made in the world. Still, we were going to hike the lands of the Bible with our esteemed teacher and have loads of adventures.

In February, we took an expedition to the Dead Sea. It was appropriately named because it is eight times saltier than the ocean, which makes it the heaviest water on earth. No living thing can survive in it. But, anyone can float in it and read a book at the same time! The Dead Sea has had many names over the millennia. Sometimes it was called the Salt Sea or the Salt Lake. Sometimes it was referred to as the Stinky Sea because the high mineral and sulphur content reeks of the smell of rotten eggs. I remember when we got to the mouth of the Jordan River that feeds the Dead Sea, I saw piles of dead fish.

"They die as soon as they reach the sea because of the heavy concentration of salt. It's too bad they can't divert the fish before they reach the delta," Charles speculated. The odor of rotting fish guts mixed with sulphur made my eyes tear.

But it is a glorious body of water too, as long as you pinch your nose while you look upon it, which is what I did when I wasn't rowing. I could see the huge cliffs—hundreds of feet tall—that surrounded the sea and plummeted straight into the water. It reminded me of a huge bath basin. When I first saw the water's hues of aqua, light greens, rusts, and all the shades of blue, I gasped. It was so beautiful. All the minerals in the lake make that effect.

The Dead Sea - photo by Nathaniel Schmidt, 1905

"There are over a hundred miles of white crystals of salt rimming the perimeter. We are going to have to be very careful, those sharp edges might puncture our boat," Charles said. He was the most pragmatic of us all, always thinking about how things worked and what we should pay attention to, which we often ignored anyway.

"But look how beautiful!" I exclaimed. Hugging the rocks and cliffs surrounding the sea were spiky sculptures that the salt had created. It was truly a magnificent natural wonder.

We desperately wanted to go to this incredible place with its strange landscape and Biblical significance. And we wanted to be the first Westerners to successfully circumnavigate the Dead Sea in a rowboat! We had already glimpsed it in December while on a short hike from Jerusalem. Before we went there, we had been warned of all the dangers by nearly everyone who talked to us and everything we read about the area. Some earlier explorers had died from dehydration at the sea. Other accounts told of boats being smashed into the cliffs when a sudden, violent storm whipped up and killed the men aboard.. There were also reports of people attacked by savages or wild animals. One of our travel guides, *Palestine and Syria: Handbook for Travelers* (Third edition, 1898), edited by Karl Baedeker, explained:

> The desert proper is safer than the borderland between it and the cultivated country. Its confines are infested with marauders of all kinds…Predatory attacks are occasionally made on travelers by Bedouins from remote districts, but only when the attacking party is more powerful. To use one's weapons in such cases may lead to serious consequences, as the traveler who kills an Arab immediately exposes himself to the danger of retaliation from the whole tribe.

We knew it was a risky undertaking, but figured we could take every precaution. We'd bring lots of water so as not to dehydrate. And we'd keep our eyes on the barometer to gauge when a storm was approaching, so we could be on land before gale winds picked up. Being in a boat seemed like a very safe bet for other reasons too.

Since the water was undrinkable and there were no fish in the sea, the Bedouin had no reason to be on the water. They were not traders; they had a semi-nomadic life eating what game they could hunt on the desert while remaining in their own territory. Therefore, they had no boats and most had never seen one in their entire lives. So we could always escape onto the water—any potential attackers could not follow us there. Our strategy was to keep a careful watch while we explored the shores and inland areas. If one of us saw a native, we would alert the others, leap into our boat and simply push off into the sea.

"At night, while we sleep near the shore, we will each take turns watching for wild animals or potential marauders," the Prof informed us. "We will take two-to-three-hour shifts until morning." It was a reasonable plan.

At the mouth of the Jordan, there was a monastery where we were able to find a sixteen-foot-long rowboat. A special permit from the government had to be secured for us to rent it, which delayed our excursion a few days. The officials told us it was simply too dangerous to go to the Dead Sea but we were persistent and did get the permit.

The Prof named the boat the *Dagmar* after his little girl [my grandmother]. The *Dagmar* had one pair of oars, a rudder and a sail. In that boat, we put food and water for three weeks for four people. Our cameras, tripods, surveying equipment, reference books, maps, papers, camping equipment and blankets were all packed in it. "We have no room to bring a change of clothes; we will remain in what we are wearing for the whole trip," the Prof said. We knew he was right, for I saw the boat piled up with all our gear.

It was a great trip. Our first day, we explored the thermal hot springs that burst from the cliffs and cascaded down the steep rock face. Because Cleopatra visited there, I pretended to be the Queen bathing in the steamy pools while her maidens fixed her hair. I swooned and sighed. Charles dunked me under the water and the others just laughed at my plight. I yelled for King Herod to rescue me, which only made them guffaw some more. Then Olmstead meandered off, without having lunch, to find the place where a certain woman named Salome danced for the King.

A few days later, after we had rowed down the shore and climbed up through the waterfalls in the great River Arnon, it was my turn to watch the boat while the Prof, Olmstead and Charles walked up the beach. They found some Roman ruins, an ancient aqueduct and the remains of two houses. Being an archeologist, you can imagine how sad I was to have missed that! Anyway, the others were very excited. They had been engrossed in taking notes, measurements and photographs when Charles spotted on the cliffs an Arab man wrapped in linen cloth looking down at them.

Of course, they thought this could be a scout for the marauders, who would alert his clan to return and attack them. They grabbed the cameras and equipment and scurried back to the boat. I helped them toss the supplies into the *Dagmar* and we shoved off into the sea. But this was precisely the wrong time to be on the great salt lake. We were right beside the Lisan

Peninsula, a four-mile jetty that protruded out into the water. Its cliffs ran perpendicular to the Dead Sea and a storm was rolling in. The winds whipped up, coming out of the north, pushing our boat into the cliffs. This was one of the serious dangers we had desperately tried to avoid. We rowed with all our might to keep from being thrown up into that sheer jagged rock wall that rises hundreds of feet straight up.

To make matters worse, our boat had sprung some leaks. The day before, Charles had tried to fix the holes by heating up some black pitch that littered the edges of the sea, but it didn't hold. We had to furiously bail water out of our vessel. By now the sky had grown dark. We looked over at the beach. The fire torches the Bedouin were carrying moved slowly back and forth on the shore. Obviously they were looking for us. Never would they have suspected that we were actually on the sea, in a boat, during a storm, in the night. They must have been scratching their beards in wonder at our disappearance.

By the time we had fought the wind and waves enough to reach beyond the peninsula and the danger of being smashed against it, it was completely dark. There was no place to go. We certainly couldn't go south because of the huge cliffs of the Lisan and we couldn't go north, where the Bedouin were. There was no choice but to cross the sea in our leaky boat with waves that were taller than our skiff and crashing in on us. It was made more laborious by the fact that the waves were like lead due to the heavy saturation of salt. We took turns bailing water from the boat while two others, with one oar each, rowed. I made some silent prayers to God; I wasn't sure we would make it there alive, but the Prof insisted we would.

Somehow, Professor Schmidt navigated us across the surrounding blackness. I don't know how he did it. I think he had the spirit of a homing pigeon in him. Eight grueling hours later we made it across the sea to the western shore. We were drenched, cold, exhausted. But we could see the fires of another tribal camp, so we pushed on north a mile or two further. Then we saw the campfires of yet another camp. At the end of our limits we paddled north another mile or two.

Finally, we found a deserted wadi river bed where we could land the boat. It was a quiet, dark spot. Since we had no change of clothes, we passed a rather cold, wet February night. By this time, our clothes were shredded from all the jagged salt rocks. Sleeves were missing; gaping holes in the pant legs testified that we had been wearing them while we climbed and hiked day and night. They were not warm, but at least we were wearing more than fig leaves! We no longer had shoes on because the salt had shrunken them and made them useless. Our feet were bloodied as we made our way onto the rough stones on the shore. Yet, we still had to take turns keeping guard through the night, but I don't think we did such a good job.

At sunrise, we stoked up our fire and began to boil water for coffee, when we saw a friendly-looking man come over the ridge. Was he one of the savages we had been told to fear? I wasn't sure. He had a broad smile that showed his broken teeth and a thin frame with light mahogany skin, and he wore a small cloth about his waist. He didn't look very threatening to me. Rather, he looked somewhat malnourished. The Prof greeted him, picking up the man's dialect quickly. I tried to catch the gist of what was said. Soon after, the visitor left.

"He says he is from the Rashidy tribe at Ein Gedi," the Prof informed us. But, there was something strange. Professor Schmidt noticed that the man had left to the south, which seemed curious because he had calculated that Ein Gedi lay to the north.

About one hour later, twenty-one Bedouin men charged over the sand. They swarmed at us, wearing almost no clothing; some were even naked. This was a common practice to make them look more fearsome, which it did! And it also prevented their clothing being snagged on rocks, I speculated. Each one was brandishing a weapon. They held guns, knives, swords, pistols and spears. Seeing this, we quickly heaved our things in the *Dagmar* and pushed off into the sea. Unfortunately, we didn't get far enough, for the beach happened to be shallow at the spot we had camped. The war party blasted into the water, grabbed our boat and dragged it back to shore. At gun point, they took our food and blankets.

I was sure this was the end. My heart was pounding so loud, I thought the natives could hear it. Then the Prof did something that startled even us. He stood straight and erect, as always, as if nothing unusual—like our impending death—was happening! He spoke in his most sermon-like voice.

"It seems that you are not of the Rashidy Tribe as you pretend to be. And you are not from the village of Ein Gedi either. You are of the Jahalin tribe. Your camp is in the area called Sufasif. It is behind the tall rock escarpment that juts out beyond the ridge." He went on to tell them in detail about their hideout. We had never even been there ourselves!

You should have seen those warriors' mouths drop open and their eyes widen. They stepped back a bit and slowly lowered their weapons as the Prof spoke. Who was this man, this white man with funny clothes on, who washed up on their shore? Who was this foreign man who knew their language, their dialect, who knew who they were, where they lived? This was no ordinary person. What else did he know?

Nathaniel Schmidt told them about the places we had been. He told them about the thermal hot springs that blew steam out of the top of the cliffs. How we soaked in the hot pools until our skin turned red. How I pretended to be Queen Cleopatra bathing there! The tribesmen laughed. He told them about finding the palace where a woman had danced for the King and had received a most unusual gift.

As he talked, the Prof slowly moved over to the campfire we had made. He added a twig to stoke the dying embers to life again. Soon a full fire was going. One by one those desert dwellers sat down to listen to him. We did too. Olmstead, Charles and I looked at each other. It was a miracle. The Jahalin people were known to be a fierce warrior tribe. And there they were, quiet and entranced by the Prof, sitting around the campfire listening to his tales.

He told them about the River Arnon with its tall cliffs and how we took our boat upstream against the current and over the waterfalls. They picked up the end of our boat to look underneath. It didn't have legs! It seemed preposterous to them, they didn't understand how the boat moved. What made it go? It was a mystery. Those tribesmen sat very still, eyes fastened on us.

The Prof told them about places we had not even been yet, like the great white mountain with the figure made of salt that is called Lot's wife. "You know these stories too?" they asked, surprised that this white man should know their own legends. Professor Schmidt made them tea, loading the pot with lots of sugar, in true Arab custom, all the while acting as though they were merely welcome guests who happened to stumble on to our camp.

They chided us for our funny clothing. We really did look quite ridiculous in our completely tattered ensembles. The Prof bellowed and we all took our cue to join him in laughing at ourselves. And, I was the most convincing!

The leader of the war party, with his white beard and sharp eyes, got to his feet. "You are a Master!" He spoke as though the realization had just come to him. There was much murmuring and heads bobbed in agreement. Then they stood up in turn, those naked warriors, and saluted him! The elder of the tribe reached out and took Professor Schmidt's face in his rough hands and kissed him on each cheek. The others followed in suit with glimmering eyes in awe of this white man. Olmstead, Charles and I sat stunned, witnessing this scene. I was bursting with pride as my eyes began to water. "You are a great man!" the Bedouin pronounced.

The morning had progressed, the sun now hovering over the eastern hills of the Dead Sea reflecting those brilliant greens and shades of aqua on the still waters. The leader of the tribe announced, "You can go now. We will not harm you." As the men motioned for us to go, Charles, Olmstead and I darted smiles to each other—we were elated. We could finally leave our captors! But, oh no, not the Prof, he had another plan in mind. He held up his hands in protest.

"We are just meeting new friends, getting to know each other and having such a nice visit, we will stay a while longer," the professor informed the tribesmen. We had the chance to go and our teacher didn't think it was a good idea! I could have screamed. Olmstead put his hand on my shoulder as I sat patiently, trying to keep my nerves from frying.

The Prof had his motives, which he later told us. He didn't want to give the impression that we were eager to leave. He didn't want to let on that we were at all anxious. Was he ever a good actor! So we stayed a while longer. Finally, the tribal leaders insisted. They picked up our belongings and put them back in the *Dagmar*. Of course, they kept the sugar and lemons, which were rare treats.

We waved and smiled at each other as we took off in our leaky boat. The sun was shining, and I thought, *They don't look like savages to me anymore. Why, they look like friends.*

Why, they look like friends. Friends. I said the word to myself again. *Yes—just people. Just like me.* Though tears filled my eyes, I rowed on because I could see much more clearly now.

Epilogue

Albert Olmstead, Jesse Wrench and Benson Charles all graduated from Cornell in 1906, Olmstead with a PhD.

The following year, Olmstead led a new expedition to the Orient joined again by Wrench and Charles. As official members of the *Cornell Expedition to Asia Minor and the Assyro-Babylonian Orient*, they trekked for eighteen months through what was then referred to as the Turkish Empire. The much awaited publication, *Travels and Studies in the Nearer East: Hittite Inscriptions,* was published upon their return.

Jesse Wrench became a Professor of European History at the University of Missouri and founded the Missouri Archeology Society. He was a very loved and flamboyant character on campus wearing his long cape and beret with an occasional flower tucked behind his ear. *Time Magazine* dubbed him "Mr. University of Missouri." He married and had one daughter.

Benson Charles received his Doctorate in Philosophy in 1910 from the University of Pennsylvania and taught Semitics. In his early forties, he moved back to his hometown, where he joined the family construction business and married. He had one daughter.

Albert Olmstead became a Professor of Oriental History at the Oriental Institute of the University of Chicago. He wrote several books and many articles, becoming a well-respected scholar in his field. In1936, he returned to the Near East, this time as Director of the American School of Oriental Study in Bagdad. He married and had three daughters. The eldest became a scholar, following in her father's footsteps.

After returning to Ithaca from the expedition, Nathaniel Schmidt's four-year-old son, Thor, died. Nonetheless, Schmidt continued his intensive activities: lecturing around the county, teaching, writing and participating in many organizations. His speaking and advocacy work with the women's suffrage and the Ethical Culture movements helped to further those causes. He wrote hundreds of articles and several books. In 1924, Schmidt returned to the Orient to travel and research. In the summers he visited his married daughter, Dagmar, and her family. They went swimming and boating in the bay.

Eliud Nieves De La Rosa

 My story begins humbly in the bucolic countryside of Puerto Rico's west coast where a choir of exotic birds sang the best songs never written to a golden rising sun, which in turn set the coffee blossoms ablaze with its radiance. My story then travels to New York City, Southeast Asia, back to NY, then to Florida and NY again. My wish is that my story and yours will live in the hearts and on the lips of someone for as long as lovers love and dreamers dream.

Eliud Nieves De La Rosa is a visual artist, writer and storyteller. His love for stories began as a toddler. His mother, Maria Miguelina De La Rosa De Nieves, an avid reader and teller of stories, always told him a bedtime story. When she didn't have one she would just make one up.

While teaching in Florida, Eliud founded the Brevard County Storytelling Festival for children. The past few summers he has headed a storytelling camp for children in Ovid, NY. He tells folk tales, fairy tales, multicultural tales and original stories. He and his wife Merideth perform as the storytelling duo *And 2 Make 3*.

Eliud Nieves De La Rosa
Ithaca, New York
www.and2make3.com
and2make3@gmail.com

The Selfish King

Eliud Nieves De La Rosa

Once there was an alabaster castle that towered above all the trees that surrounded it. Its shiny walls glimmered in the sunlight. The selfish king who inhabited that castle stood by a window motionless, staring into the deep green forest. He possessed all the power and wealth that any ruler could ever hope for. But the one thing that he coveted the most had always eluded him. The one thing that he could not get his greedy hands on was the most beautiful bird that the world had ever known.

This bird was a dove the color of new fallen snow with delicate shades of moonlight. Its soft black eyes shone like rare pearls found in the deepest ocean. Its cry was not mournful but soothing and inspiring. It sang of hopes and possibilities.

The people of this kingdom loved this dove that dwelled atop an olive tree in the middle of the forest. They would often gather at the foot of the giant olive to listen to the songs of this special creature. Parents would hold their children quietly as they listened reverently. Old people wept without knowing why. All they knew was that the song and the sight of this bird made them glad they were alive.

The king walked away from the window and slammed his fist on a table. Right then and there he vowed that he would own the one thing that he did not possess. He called for his top generals, promising glory and fame to the one who could bring the beautiful dove to him.

The generals looked at each other in disbelief. They were concerned because they knew how much the people loved this unique creature; however, they had no choice but to follow orders. The armies went into the forest with their sights set on medals and promotions. The soldiers, like a devastating wildfire, destroyed everything in their paths because that's what soldiers do. They did not stop until they came to the large olive tree. Then, methodically, they began to chop it down.

Little by little, the mighty tree began to lean until it came crashing down to the forest floor. All the nearby creatures had to flee for their lives. The soldiers searched the mangled branches until they found the stunned bird. One of them grabbed it; it did not resist. Its eyes were closed and its tiny heart beat faintly and sadly.

The king was elated when the soldier presented him with his new trophy. The selfish monarch placed a gold star on the soldier's chest and threw the confused dove into a wrought iron cage. He gave it some food and water then walked away.

The next morning the king went to the room where the dove was caged. The frightened bird was more alert by now but its eyes spoke of sadness. The selfish ruler sat in a fancy chair and demanded a song. None came. No matter how much the monarch commanded and bellowed, the bird did not sing. The frustrated king stormed out of the room.

Every morning the king returned but the results were always the same; the dove would make no sound. One day the selfish king noticed that the colors of the bird's feathers were changing from beautiful white to dull gray. Its eyes were changing as well. The shine had gone out of them. They now resembled the cold lackluster black of the wrought iron cage. The dove looked as if it were dying.

As the selfish king looked out of his window he saw that the people of the kingdom were also different. They walked around as if in a trance. The monarch did not understand what was happening. He ran to the street and tried to get people to talk to him, but they ignored him as if he were invisible. They made no sound and walked as if they were more dead than alive.

The king then spotted a beggar child sitting against a storefront. His pale face, sunken and gray, and his large black eyes spoke of lost hopes and broken dreams. The young boy glanced up at the king and, in between gasping breaths, muttered, "Let it go. Set it free so we may all live." When he heard that, the king looked at his own reflection in a store window and, to his horror, he saw that he looked just like everyone else, pale with sad and cold wrought-iron eyes. He immediately returned to the castle, ran to the room where he kept the dove and opened the cage door.

The dove looked like a statue; it did not move. After a few long moments, it took a few feeble steps to leave the cage. It lifted its wings as if to fly, but fell weakly to the floor. The king picked it up gently and placed it on the sill of an open window. As soon as the streaks of sunlight reached the dove, its color and luster returned. Even the once-sad eyes appeared to dance in the sunlight. The bird looked back at the king, whose pale and crestfallen face was now streaked with tears, and sang the most beautiful song the monarch's royal ears had ever heard. It then lifted its wings and took to the sky, and the king watched it as it disappeared into the patchwork of clouds.

It is said that in this kingdom hopes and dreams filled the hearts of all, including the once-selfish king. The alabaster castle was demolished and in its place an olive grove was planted where the dove and all its descendants sing to the people to this very day, filling their hearts with hope and peace.

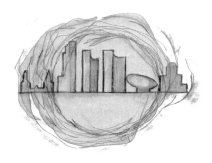

The Tater-Tater Man

Eliud Nieves De La Rosa

Have you ever heard of the Tater-Tater Man? I'm surprised you haven't because he is quite famous in these parts. Some people say that he was a "legend in the baking." He was born, or should I say grown, just a few miles from here.

You see, there was a farmer here in Lansing named Asa who lived with his wife Beatrice, whom everybody called Bea, his hound dog Ellington and his cat Gumby. Asa and Bea grew many things on their Lansing farm but their main crop was potatoes. They were quite well-known for the different kinds of potatoes they grew.

One particular potato harvesting season, a peculiar thing happened. They were harvesting their potatoes, as usual, but there was one potato that Bea couldn't pull out of the ground. No matter how hard she tried, it wouldn't come out. Bea called Asa over and together they pulled but nothing happened. They dug but it still wouldn't come out. So Asa tied a strong rope to the potato plant and hitched it to the tractor. Finally that big old tater came out of the ground.

What they saw shocked them both. This potato was not only huge, but it was shaped like a man. It had arms and legs and a big old head with quite a few eyes. Bea and Asa looked at each other in disbelief. "That's one fine tater man," said Asa.

Bea nodded and added, "Dinner is going to be quite special tonight." The two farmers carried that unusual potato into the house and put him in the kitchen sink to wash. He didn't exactly fit, but they tried. When they had washed him as best they could, they placed him on the kitchen counter.

Asa went back outside to finish up some chores and Bea began chopping vegetables to make a big pot of stew. As usual, Bea had her kitchen TV on, watching action movies. They were having a Bruce Lee marathon. *Hi-Yah!* Bruce Lee was the greatest martial artist of action movies of all time. Bea loved Bruce Lee and all his karate moves.

She started putting all of her vegetables in a large pot of boiling water, almost forgetting that she had a special ingredient for her stew. So she walked over to the counter to get her tater man. As she reached for him he winked at her with all of his eyes, jumped off the counter and ran for the door. Bea yelled, "Stop Tater Man!"

But he just laughed and said, "They dug me up to slice me and throw me in a pan, they didn't know they couldn't cook the Tater-Tater Man."

Out the door ran the Tater Man. Asa was feeding the chickens when he saw the Tater Man run by. "Stop!" yelled Asa.

But the Tater Man kept running, saying, "They dug me up to slice me and throw me in a pan, they didn't know they couldn't cook the Tater-Tater Man." On ran the Tater Man.

He soon ran past the hound dog, Ellington, who was sniffing around some bushes. Ellington yelled, "Stop, Tater Man, stop!"

But the Tater Man just laughed and said, "They dug me up to slice me and throw me in a pan, they didn't know they couldn't cook the Tater-Tater Man." On ran the Tater Man.

It wasn't long until he came up to Gumby, the cat, who was sitting on a fence. Gumby yelled, "Stop, Tater Man. Stop!"

But the Tater Man just said, "They dug me up to slice me and throw me in a pan, they didn't know they couldn't cook the Tater-Tater Man." On ran the Tater Man.

Now the Tater-Tater Man was getting quite tired when he came right up to the shore of Cayuga Lake. Tater Man had never learned to swim and he didn't quite know what to do. Suddenly Coyote came out of nowhere and said, "Hello, Tater-Tater Man. I'll help you get across the lake." The Tater Man was a bit nervous, but what choice did he have?

Coyote jumped in the lake and the Tater-Tater Man hopped on his back. But the water rose higher and higher and the coyote said, "Oh Tater Man, I would feel so sad if you got wet. Hop onto my tail." Tater Man hopped onto Coyote's tail which was raised above his back.

They continued crossing the lake, but the water rose higher and higher. And Coyote said, "Oh Tater Man, I would feel so sad if you got wet. Hop onto my head." Tater Man hopped onto Coyote's head, but the water rose higher and higher. "Oh I would feel so sad if you got wet, hop onto my nose," said Coyote.

The Tater Man hopped and Coyote smacked his lips as he prepared to eat that yummy tater. But as the Tater-Tater Man came down—*Hi-Yah!* He gave Coyote a karate chop to the snout and he did a somersault in the air and landed on the western shore of Cayuga Lake.

You see, Bea wasn't the only one who was a Bruce Lee fan. On ran the Tater Man and as far as I know, he is still running.

Merideth Nieves

I have been known for my vivid imagination and dramatic storytelling since childhood. I have fond memories of impromptu family performances with my sisters, larger-than-life accounts of everyday life, and frequent attempts to weasel my way out of a mess with wild tales. Sometimes being a storyteller can get you into trouble!

As an elementary school music teacher for fifteen years, I used all forms of performance with my students, including storytelling. I am a professional vocalist and I frequently use music—often original—to enhance my storytelling.

I live in Ithaca, NY and tell stories locally or I will travel far and wide to share my stories. I tell fairy tales, folk tales, modern stories, multicultural tales and even the often-quirky stories of my childhood and family.

My husband Eliud Nieves and I tell stories together. We call ourselves *And 2 Make 3*. We each have our own style and often work together using music or telling stories in tandem. You can find out more about us at our website.

Merideth Nieves
Ithaca, New York
www.and2make3.com
and2make3@gmail.com

Taming the Night

Merideth Nieves

In "Taming the Night," I tell the story of Anna, my petite, tougher-than-nails grandmother, who was a one of a kind with an incredible heart. Her brimming capacity for love and devotion enveloped creatures both big and small. She was a humble servant to the neglected, abandoned and weak.

When I was a child, we visited in the summers, staying in her house for up to a month at a time, turning her quiet world upside down. One summer, my grandmother told us a tale that had such a great impact me that I have always cherished it and its message that all animals, great and small, deserve love and compassion; not just the ones that we adopt into our families as pets but all of the world's living beings.

One may question Anna's decision in this story, but her motive was crystal clear. See for yourself. Her story of one particularly cold winter night in Northern Michigan speaks to her unique and limitless efforts to protect those she loved.

Anna, my petite, tougher-than-nails grandmother, walked home from the factory where she had worked since her three daughters were young children. She carried the metal lunch pail that held the sandwich and piece of fruit that made up her midday meal every day for thirty years. The snow was falling lightly, but she knew she was in for a tough walk home. Most nights in the Northern Michigan winter were trying, but everyone at work was talking about the forecast that the overnight would be particularly cold, particularly harsh. There was already something in the air. She could feel the dampness clear to her bones that made her feel older than her sixty-two years. The sky was growing darker. The stunning velvet clouds moved purposefully across the sky above her. If she wasn't so worried about the pets she'd left outside for the day, she would revel in how beautiful the sky was.

As she neared her little white house, she could see that the light dusting was turning into an iridescent blanket covering the already snowy lawn. She thought about her cherished pets, the menagerie of stray cats and dogs that she had rescued over the years. Did she know how many there were? She had three dogs but countless cats. As she walked through the front door and placed her lunch pail on the oak buffet that stood watch in the kitchen, she smiled and reminisced about how she came to be known as The Cat Lady. It was an affectionate name given to her by the many neighbors who came to know her as a great lover of all animals, but especially, the stray and abused cats that came her way. Some wandered into her yard, homeless. Others were anonymously left on her porch as kittens by those who knew she would care for them.

All of these animals lived outside, as did an old horse. My grandmother worried about them all on this exceptionally cold winter's night. She wondered whether they would last the night with the temperature dropping so abruptly and so unusually low. Rather than go about the business of making her dinner, her usual routine, she sat down in her most comfortable chair to think—the over-stuffed, red chenille yard sale find with the red-braided trim across the bottom. There really was nothing to think about. She knew what she must do. And since she hadn't yet taken the time to remove her winter gear, she went outside with the intention of corralling the three dogs and the many, many cats and bringing them in for the night. The dogs were tied; bringing them in would be an easy task. But chasing down and catching all of those cats would be next to impossible. Still, she had to try.

The dogs proved to be a little more challenging than my grandma had anticipated. To speed up her work she gathered them all by their tethers and led them together to the front door in unison; only it was far from a unified effort on their parts. In their excitement they jumped and pulled in three different directions and even her focused determination to get them inside couldn't keep her from being jerked abruptly from side to side. It was all she could do to avoid falling in the deepening snow.

After leading the dogs into the house, my grandmother set about finding the cats, one by one, catching them and setting them free just inside the front door. It seemed to take forever. Her hand-knitted gloves, although warm, did little to protect her from the scratching of the more than reluctant cats. The skittish animals ran and hid as she got close. When she thought she had found and caught the last one, she let her go in the house and went outside for one last look. There seemed to be no more hidden cats. But as she turned to head back inside, she noticed the small brown horse she affectionately called Pony standing just inside the small metal shed which was her only shelter. My grandmother paused as she thought about this. She quickly assessed the situation: inadequate shelter on a night with record-breaking low temperatures. She had no choice but to move that horse to a warmer place. There was nothing else to consider.

She called to her dear, sweet mare and reassured her that she was going to take care of her. Then she made a large opening in the wire fencing and led her horse out toward the house. Now she knew that Pony would not fit through the front door, so the two headed toward the back of the house. The small mare had never been out of her pen and was confused and reluctant, making this effort very difficult. My grandmother tugged at the bridle, but once they were out of the pen, it was hard to get the nervous horse to move. The two inched their way toward the back door, Grandma cooing sweet sounds at her horse and Pony reluctantly cooperating. And if my grandmother thought she struggled getting *to* the back door, she did not know what she was going to be up against trying to get her little horse *through* the back door and into the house.

She got in front of Pony, in the doorway, and planting her feet squarely beneath her shoulders, began to pull at the bridle, gently coaxing her horse with a quiet, almost purring, voice. But Pony didn't move. Grandma kept pulling, her words and her tone getting more impatient, more frantic. After all, she was trying to *help* this silly horse. Couldn't the old girl see that? She finally gave up on pulling and squeezed her way past her dear friend, back outside, and got behind her. Now this was very chancy. But my grandmother had no choice. She pushed fervently from the back. After a few seconds and some steady pushing, the stubborn, nervous horse shifted her weight. But instead of moving forward, she backed up just enough to send Grandma tumbling to the icy ground.

Suddenly Grandma felt all of the aches and pains of the evening, of her efforts and of her age. Despite the pain that came with the chilling numbness that was beginning to settle into her body, she sat for a moment collecting herself and calming her well-known ornery impatience. The snow had stopped, but the temperature had dropped considerably by this time, adding to the intense discomfort she was feeling. When she was ready to give it another try, she stood up—slowly and deliberately. She took a firm stance behind her beloved mare and began a gentle, steady push. The horse finally relented with a grunt of resignation and stepped onto the back porch.

Grandma led Pony inside, toward the front of the house. The final, most difficult challenge was over. The two friends maneuvered from room to room, bumping walls and door frames and tripping over furniture. Sweet Pony whinnied cries of nervousness with every bump. But she seemed to surrender her stubbornness, if not her apprehension, and to trust my grandmother. When they made it through the back bedroom, the kitchen and then finally to the living room, the chunky brown horse stood, like a statue, in front of the sofa, steam rising from her back. My grandmother sat down in her most comfortable chair and just watched all of her darlings. The dogs lay peacefully, clumps of snow matted to their fur slowly melting on the faded Oriental rug. Some cats were nowhere to be seen as they hid, terrified, in secrets places throughout the house. Others darted back and forth with the excitement of little children at a new playground. Pony stood, swaying nearly imperceptibly at first and then attempting to turn slowly around the room as she surveyed her strange surroundings. Grandma spoke to her as if conversation was in order, as she often spoke to all of her furry children. She smiled to herself in her exhaustion. She had been successful in bringing in all of her beloved animals, out of harm's way. She had been triumphant in taming the night; this night.

Anna Burchard, circa 1962

The Bullfrogs and the Big Race

Merideth Nieves

"The Bullfrogs and the Big Race" is my adaptation of a folktale that I discovered and fell in love with whose author remains unknown to me. It is a tale that speaks to the importance of the words we choose to speak and their impact on those around us.

The Honey Island River Swamp is one of those places strewn on either side with rickety, makeshift houseboats. Other than that it is unspoiled by the touch of humanity. You could make many a sweet memory meandering down that still and mysterious water in your pontoon boat, your best pal, your old hound, by your side. It is just that kind of lazy place. The river swamp runs through the woods, full of giant oaks and cypress drenched in delicate Spanish moss, which makes the trees not only look majestic but also mysterious.

The Bayou is home to all kinds of creatures, big and small. And if you don't mess with 'em, they don't mess with you; birds, bugs, ground dwellers, tree dwellers and well…you know. I've wandered these woods since I was a kid and I know every inch in these parts. Well…enough about how much I love the place, been here all my life. It's really for them animals. And I respect that. Probably the toughest part about being out here is those mosquitoes. But I respect them, too. They must be here for a reason I figure.

I'll get to my point. Strange things go on around here. I'm not talking about the witchcraft or anything. I'm talking about wonderful, miraculous things; things you might not see anywhere else.

You see, there once was a bunch of big old bullfrogs that lived in these waters who decided to have a running competition. (This is how the story goes, and I believe it.) The goal was to reach the top of a very tall tree. They found the tallest tree around. It had been dead a long time with barely a branch left on its trunk.

110

A big crowd of animals gathered from all over these parts just to watch the race. Some stood around the tree and some stayed in the water, near the edge. There were a few snapping turtles who ventured out of the water to have a look. A few deer wandered from further in the woods to get a closer view. Dozens of excited grasshoppers hopped to the nearby low bushes and the rather subdued slugs parked themselves beneath that dense, protective hedge to stay clear of all the larger animals.

All kinds of birds gathered in the neighboring trees with the fox squirrels: grackles, mourning doves, kill deer, crows and a pair of wood ducks, the male calling, "Jeeer," the female calling, "Oo-eeek." The water birds—the egrets, the cranes and the herons—stayed wading in the shallow waters near the riverbank with the crayfish, the diamond back water snakes and those mean-lookin' alligators, who for the life of me I can't remember ever doing anything to anyone, for all their dubious reputation.

With the audience in position and the big old bullfrogs ready, the race began. The bullfrogs were ablaze with energy and excitement. As the glistening green frogs climbed, they would call, "JUG-A-RUM! JUG-A-RUM!"

Honestly, no one in the crowd really believed that those clumsy, awkward-looking bullfrogs would reach the top of that old tree. They called out things like:

"Oh…WAY too difficult!"

"They will NEVER make it to the top!"

"Not a chance they will succeed. The tree is too tall!"

Those big, strong bullfrogs began collapsing. One by one… Except for those who, in a fresh burst of energy, were climbing higher and higher.

The crowd continued to yell: "It's too difficult! No one will make it!"

Illustration by
Eliud Nieves De La Rosa

More of those frogs got tired, gave up and fell from the tree. The rest continued to call out exhausted and breathless: "Jug-a-rum… jug-a-rum."

But ONE continued higher and higher and higher. She wouldn't give up! At the end, everyone else had given up climbing the tall, dead tree except for the one big green bullfrog who, after a monumental effort, was the only one to reach the top!

All of the other frogs naturally wanted to know how this one frog managed to do it. And so did all of the animals who were watching. So they all gathered in close as one of the racers asked her how she had found the strength to reach the goal.

It turned out the winner was deaf!

You see, this story was told to me by my Ma and to her by hers. Everyone around here knows about the bullfrog who reached the top because she thought she could and because she couldn't hear anyone tell her she couldn't.

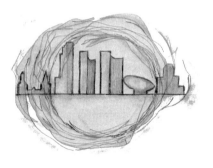

Claire Nolan

Storytelling and stories have always resonated with me but it wasn't until I attended a Tellabration performance that I realized this was an art form that I could practice. At first, I told literary and folk and fairy tales, then I began to mine memories of growing up in a large family. Memories and dreams often blend. Family stories take on lives of their own as each family member relates what they saw and heard and thought about a particular event. When the audience asks, "Is it true? Did it really happen?" I begin to wonder if it was all a dream—until my mother and siblings assure me that, yes, it really *did* happen! I continue to tell literary stories and folk and fairy tales. As a teacher of English as a Second Language, I find that storytelling is an excellent tool in the classroom. My students from all over the world have shared many stories including creation myths, trickster tales and personal stories—and my life and art are richer for it.

Claire Nolan
Guilderland, New York
cbnolou@gmail.com
518-209-6477

Growing Up Nolan

Part One—My Brothers

Claire Nolan

Not last night but the night before
Twenty four robbers came knocking at my door
As I went out…to let them come in…
This is what they said to me:
Spanish Dancer do the high kick
Spanish Dancer do the low split
Spanish Dancer turn around
Spanish Dancer touch the ground
Spanish Dancer get out of town!

When I was seven years old, I was a Spanish Dancer and I lived with my family at 22 Winthrop Avenue in Albany, NY. Our house was perfect. It had a big front porch where my sisters and I would sit on rocking chairs, our feet propped up on the railings. We'd read comic books all summer long—comic books and Mad Magazine when we could get them.

Our front lawn was bisected by a walkway and, on the front walk that led up to our steps, my sisters and I played hopscotch and jumped rope—and each of us had a turn at being a Spanish Dancer.

If you looked up the street towards Washington Avenue, you could see endless rows of identical front lawns. That was the no man's land where the boys played Army and Wild West and Cops and Robbers and every one of them was armed. They had cap guns and water pistols and machine guns and even bows and arrows and, when he was old enough, each boy got a BB gun. My brother Ed was 14 years old and he had a BB gun.

That summer of 1964, my mother was pregnant with my youngest brother, Paul. It was a difficult pregnancy and her doctor told her that she should lie down and rest in bed—*all* day.

My mother had eight children and staying in bed all day posed a bit of a problem, but she was too polite to say anything to the doctor. So she asked our friend, Helen, to come and stay with us. Helen was a registered nurse and well qualified for the job of helping my mother rest in bed. But best of all we loved Helen and she loved us and there wasn't anything she wouldn't do for us.

Helen made my mother comfortable in her bedroom which had two windows that looked out over our backyard and another window that looked out on the driveway where we played endless games of kickball all summer long. If the ball landed on the top of our flat garage roof it was a home run and if it hit our house it was a foul ball. Every single foul ball hit the exact same spot on the house—right under my mother's bedroom window. WHUMP!! My mother could hear us: "That's a foul ball!" "FOUL BALL!!" "You're OUT!!" "IT'S A HOME RUN!!" I don't know how she got any rest. But my mother never complained—not once!

We played other games in the driveway: Red Rover, Mother May I? and Red Light, Green Light, and we rode our bikes in the driveway too. Our bikes were magical machines made of steel and filled with air. They could take us anywhere and everywhere. On my bike, I was a cowgirl galloping across the prairie or I was zooming down the highway on a motorcycle, VROOOM! And when it got dark we played hide and seek and our garage was home base. "Ready or not, here I come…Ally Ally in come free!" And when it was really and truly dark, one by one, the back porch lights came on and the doors opened and the mothers called us all home.

My parents never parked the car in the garage because that is where we played. In our garage we had saw horses and planks of wood; we had a chalkboard and an adding machine. We set up the planks of wood as a counter and placed the adding machine on it. That was a grocery store. The empty boxes and cans we found in the trash were our merchandise. We added up the sales on the adding machine.

Or, bored with that, we transformed the garage into a diner with the daily specials written up on the chalkboard. Our diner sold only the best food in the world: grilled cheese sandwiches and French fries, root beer floats and chocolate milkshakes. My sister, the waitress, came around to take our order using an old assignment pad she found in a box of school supplies.

In August, school was a dim yet somehow troubling memory.

Sometimes we dragged the planks of wood and the saw horses outside into our yard and we made seesaws. *Seesaw Marjorie Daw, Johnny has a new master! But he will earn just a penny a day because he can't work any faster!* Up and down in rhythm with the rhyme we went until…there I was! Frozen at the top of the seesaw. My legs dangled uselessly and I could see my sister far, far, far below, grinning up at me, and I knew what I had to do. "Monkey, monkey let me down!" I cried, and she replied, "What will you give me?" And suddenly all the wealth and treasure of the world was mine to bestow to secure my freedom. When the terms of my release were negotiated satisfactorily for both parties, my sister pushed off and down I came.

Sometimes we had to stay out of the garage because my brother Ed would set up target practice there. He placed the empty boxes and cans on the saw horses and took careful aim. He was the Lone Ranger, the Rifleman, he was John Wayne! And when he hit a box we heard WHUUMP and when he hit a can we heard PING and sometimes he hit nothing at all and that sounded like broken glass.

Once my brother Ed's BB gun jammed and Ed did what all boys do when their BB guns jam—he turned it over and peered down inside the barrel and then smacked the butt sharply on the pavement and out shot the BB! It grazed his temple and the blood spurted out!

We were shocked!

We were amazed!

We were delighted!

The adults came, seemingly out of thin air, and took him to the hospital. When he came home his head was wrapped in thick layers of gauze and he told us that if the BB had been *this* much closer to his temple, he would have died! I looked at my mother while Ed was telling us this and she wasn't smiling so I knew that Ed was telling the truth.

Our backyard was small but we had a beautiful rock garden with three walls. One wall was our neighbor's garage, and the back wall of the rock garden was the backs of two garages, the fronts of which were on Homestead Avenue. The two garages had a small space between them, a space just wide enough for a child to squeeze through. Sometimes I climbed to the top of our rock garden to look through that space and I saw all the way to Homestead Avenue.

Sometimes kids from Homestead Avenue came through that space between the garages and they appeared at the top of our rock garden.

Children from another PLANET!

And they stayed and played with us all day! As dark came on, they disappeared between the garages and we never saw them again.

Sometimes kids from Winthrop Avenue climbed to the top of our rock garden and squeezed between the two garages, and I was afraid we would never see them again, either. But they always returned. I could see them appear at dusk at the top of our rock garden looking a little dazed as though they weren't too sure where they were or where they had been.

The third wall of the rock garden was our garage, and it was an easy thing to climb to the top of our rock garden and get on to our roof. I didn't like to climb up there too often—I prefer to keep my feet firmly planted on the ground.

One day, my brother Tim decided that what he really needed was a parachute. He found a notebook and drew some designs which we all agreed were quite good. Tim went up to our mother's bedroom where she was resting and showed her the designs. My mother was delighted with the project and she told Helen where she could find some old sheets, and together my mother and Tim cut and pinned the parachute into existence and then Helen took it downstairs to sew it all together.

While Helen sewed and my mother rested, Tim made his preparations. He found an old carpet in the basement and he dragged it upstairs and placed it at the foot of the back porch steps. He practiced jumping off the porch, first from the bottom step. He progressed all the way up to the top step and then to the porch itself. He jumped off the porch and rolled gracefully and he never got hurt at all. He was ready. He dragged the carpet over to the driveway near the garage, and he went inside to find Helen. Helen gave the beautiful white parachute to Tim who carefully draped it over his shoulder so it wouldn't get dirty and he went back outside while Helen took a cup of tea up to my mother.

As Helen was passing the window overlooking the backyard, she said, "Oh look there's Tim climbing the rock garden!" And it was only then that my mother and Helen realized exactly why it was that Tim had wanted a parachute.

The two women watched as Tim reached the top of the garage. He stood there with his parachute ready. My mother could see Tim framed in her bedroom window, separated from her by a chasm of hot August air. Tim, at six, was no longer a baby, no longer her youngest. Tim was a dreamer and a planner and an adventurer ready to take his first step into the unknown!

I don't know where I was the day Tim jumped off the garage roof. Sometimes I think I was up there, on the roof with Tim, although I didn't like to be up there. I saw him step off the roof and I watched the parachute billow up like a big white marshmallow.

Sometimes I think I was standing in the driveway. With the other kids, I watched as Tim stepped off the garage and floated down to us, a smile of wonder on his upturned face.

Sometimes I think I was with my mother, in her bedroom, sitting next to her on her bed, her arm around me. I could feel my new baby brother moving gently inside her as, together, my mother and I watched Tim step off the roof.

I don't remember where I was when Tim jumped but I know that he jumped because the next day the twins who were eight and Tim and I were sent to Utica on a Greyhound bus and when we came home, everything had changed, summer was over, school was starting and we had a new baby brother.

Colette Odell

A native of Oneonta, New York, Colette Odell enjoys listening, reading, writing, and telling stories. She belongs to three local story circles and serves on the boards of Church Women United and Schenectady Interfaith. Colette tells original, family and historical stories. She has performed at Boght Arts Center, Caffé Lena, Word Plays at Proctor's Theater, various churches and private gatherings.

Colette's mother, Alice Jeannette Baxter Odell, is the Jeannette in her story. Colette remembers, as a toddler, sitting at Virginia Shaver's side on her lovely piano bench while Virginia entertained with her skills and knowledge of music. Colette credits Virginia with encouraging her to read, explore and appreciate the beauty of the world.

Now Colette passes on her love of stories, imagination and play to the joy of her heart, her grandson, Tavin Royce Odell—and she dedicates her story, *The Fork*, to him.

Colette Odell
Clifton Park, New York
518-371-0634

The Fork

Colette Odell

The young pastor stepped into Crossroads Baptist Church reporting for duty. It was his first job since graduating from Bible College and since the passing of his mother. The overworked senior pastor gave him a tour of the building, escorted him to the office he would use, and handed him a list of assignments for the first week. As the senior pastor went over the list of about a dozen items, the young pastor was excited and pleased to be asked to submit an article introducing himself for the parish newsletter and to be entrusted with creating a curriculum and leading the Thursday night Bible study. All of these tasks were things he knew he could do and enjoy except for one, which seemed especially urgent and dear to the older pastor. It was to visit and set up a regular visitation schedule with Virginia who, at 93, was the oldest member of the congregation, and in the community's heart, an old saint.

The young pastor, a top student in Bible College, quickly wrote his piece for the newsletter and accomplished the small things on his list. By his training, he knew exactly how to set up a curriculum for a Bible study, and had an overview of the course approved by the senior pastor early in the week. He had his first lesson prepared and worksheets printed by early Thursday afternoon. He had his assignments all done, all except for visiting old Virginia. He sat at his desk, hoping the pastor would ask him to do something else, for he dreaded the trip to Mease Manor Retirement Community and the chat with the old saint. He did not know any old people, as his mother had died before the age of fifty. Therefore, he thought old people were grouchy, unpleasant, and boring, but as he had nothing else to do, he reluctantly plodded up the road to the Manor.

When he got inside, he took the elevator to Virginia's floor and found her door. Assuming old people were small and stooped, he bent his knees to put his face at her level, as he rang the doorbell. Then came his first surprise, as he found himself rising to his full height to be eye to eye with the six-foot-tall lady standing before him with a wide, healthy, natural smile.

As he sat in her living room, he was amazed to see photos, paintings, and artifacts from around the world artistically displayed on every wall. He learned that afternoon that Virginia had been born and raised in her father's hotel, The Wilson, in the small central New York city of Oneonta, which had at that time, the world's largest railroad round-house. She was an only child, who met her life-long friend, Mary Chesebro Stanhouse, on their first day of school. She also had dear Oneonta cousins, Jeannette and Sheldon Baxter. The Baxter children taught Virginia skating, skiing, swimming, bowling, and tennis, although she was neither the natural athlete Sheldon was, nor the sassy tomboy Jeannette was. What pranks she and Jeannette had pulled!

Taking in as many of her heirlooms as he could, the young pastor's eyes began to rest on her lovely old piano. Without a word, Virginia slipped to the piano bench and began playing a haunting sonata. As he listened he shed a tear. Then, she moved effortlessly into a long medley of beloved old hymns that his mother taught him when he was a young child. Among them were *The Old Rugged Cross*, *In the Garden* and *Whispering Hope*. As he took in the sweetness and the power of those familiar old songs, his soul began to meet the soul of the old saint, and in some surprising way, they became family.

Suddenly, out of the corner of his eye, he caught sight of Virginia's clock and realized that he had spent the entire afternoon and that dinner time was now over. He had about a half-hour to get back to the church and welcome the Bible class members. He offered a quick prayer and sped to her door. Then he did something he never would have imagined himself doing, he hugged the dear woman and asked if he could visit next Thursday at the same time. Of course, she said, "Yes."

The young pastor ran back to the church with a singing heart.

He returned to Virginia's apartment each Thursday afternoon. These visits became the highlight of his week. They talked about their families and how each had celebrated Thanksgiving, Christmas, Easter, birthdays, and the Fourth of July. One by one, they enjoyed her photos, paintings, and artifacts. He learned a lot of history and culture as they talked about her belongings, and he learned of her education, teaching, library career, travels, missions, awards, and extensive correspondence. What she had not done to serve God, family, and community!

Some of Virginia's stories were so dear to the young pastor that he asked to hear them over and over. One of these was about how Papa had entertained Eleanor Roosevelt at The Wilson Hotel, and another about how she had sung during a week-long Billy Graham Crusade. He learned of her many charities and projects. He also discovered her fondness for homemade desserts and heard that her cousin, Jeannette, had become a first-rate cook and a great baker. No one could make a blueberry pie that popped in one's mouth like Jeannette!

After learning of Virginia's love for desserts, the young pastor started watching the church coffee hours and suppers for goodies to bring to the saint. Then he began searching out restaurants and bakeries, so he could bring her treats each week. He even acquired some recipes and made desserts in his own small kitchen. It delighted him to please her.

One Thursday, after the young pastor had been visiting Virginia for about six months, something unusual happened as he started to return to the church. Suddenly, she grabbed his arm as he stepped into the corridor and said, "Pastor, one more thing."

"Yes, dear one?" As he listened his heart sank. He could never possibly honor the request she made, for he now knew that he loved her and cherished the time they shared. But, because he did indeed love her, he finally replied sadly, "I will." Then, the young pastor plodded back to the church, where he had difficulty concentrating on the Thursday night Bible study.

Early the next week, the young pastor's cell phone rang. He listened soberly before replying, "I'll be right there." Then he went to his mother's silverware chest and studied the contents. Unlike most silver sets, his mother's tableware was a hodgepodge of unmatched items she had inherited, found, and purchased during her life. He decided on an antique silver fork with a scroll and a rose on the handle, placed the fork in his pocket, and walked to the mortuary.

When he arrived at the funeral home, the director escorted him to the preparation room, where the old saint, in her favorite dress, lay in a simple wooden casket. Lovingly, the young pastor placed the fork into her hand and bent to kiss her forehead before returning to his apartment to write the most important address of his short career at Cornerstone Baptist Church.

News of Virginia's passing spread quickly through all the Mease buildings, the church, and the region where she had lived for thirty-eight years after her retirement as Director of Libraries for a large set of school districts on Long Island. During that time, Virginia had served as President of the New York State Library Association, an honor which delighted her papa and mama, John W. and Francis C. Shaver, as neither of them, nor any of their siblings, had attended college, no less earned three college degrees and the prestige of her offices.

Soon people of various walks of life began visiting the mortuary to pay their respects to the old saint, and as they passed her casket they wondered about the fork. It was certainly an odd thing to have in one's burial box, but they signed her guest book, often writing a memory of something Virginia had said or done that made them happy or eased their burdens.

Two days later, people gathered at the church for Virginia's funeral. Since singing was one of her many passions, a Director of Music from a church in a nearby town where she and her mother had shared a house, came and lead the group in round after round of hymns and choruses that he knew Virginia loved. Then the young pastor came to the lectern. He reminded the parishioners that he came to Cornerstone a little over six months ago, young, inexperienced, and full of himself. The wise senior pastor had sent him to Virginia, so he could learn good visitation skills, but he had not only done that, he had also come to love the saint as if she were one of his own family.

Next, he acknowledged he had overheard some of the funeral home visitors discussing the fork in Virginia's hand and imagined others were curious. He told them that on his last visit with Virginia, she had asked him to place it there. He also told them that he had been sad and reluctant to say he would do it, for he did not want to think she would die. Virginia had explained the unusual request this way, "Over the course of my life, I have attended many meals at various churches, clubs, and organizations. The food has always been delightful, but toward the end of the meal, someone usually calls out, 'Hold onto your fork!' For me, that has always been the high point of the affair. I know that soon someone else will come along passing out the dessert, the best part. It may be marble cake, strawberry shortcake, or mouthwatering pie, but it is always wonderful. So, when I lie in death, the fork will be a reminder to my friends and family that, for me, as a child of God, the next phase of my life, the best part, has begun."

When I *tell* this story, at this point, I hum or sing the following hymn.

The Strife is O'er, the Battle Done

Alleluia, alleluia, alleluia!
The strife is o'er, the battle done,
the victory of life is won;
the song of triumph has begun.
Alleluia!

Alleluia, alleluia, alleluia!
The powers of death have done their worst,
but Christ their legions hath dispersed:
let shout of holy joy outburst.
Alleluia!

Alleluia, alleluia, alleluia!
The three sad days are quickly sped,
he rises glorious from the dead:
all glory to our risen Head!
Alleluia!

Alleluia, alleluia, alleluia!
He closed the yawning gates of hell,
the bars from heaven's high portals fell;
let hymns of praise his triumphs tell!
Alleluia!

Alleluia, alleluia, alleluia!
Lord! by the stripes which wounded thee,
from death's dread sting thy servants free,
that we may live and sing to thee.
Alleluia!

Words: Symphonia Sirenum Selectarum, 1695; trans.
Francis Pott (1832-1909)

In loving memory of Virginia Helen Shaver

Born: May 8, 1916, The Wilson Hotel, Oneonta, New York
Died: March 26, 2010, Mease Manor, Dunedin, Florida
Buried: April 7, 2010, Sylvan Abbey Memorial Park, Clearwater,
  Florida

A Faithful Friend and a Child of God

Gil Payette

I retell stories of Native American folklore based on my understanding of myths, legends and tales. I started telling stories with the Sabino Canyon Volunteer Naturalists in 2001, and then with Tellers-of-Tales, both in Tucson.

I have performed Native American folklore programs at Canyon Ranch Resort and Native American-themed keynote presentations for the Western National Parks Association. I have also told stories for the Arizona Historical Society, Defenders of Wildlife Festivals and the historical Empire Ranch.

I am affiliated with the Story Circle of the Capital District in upstate New York. In this publication, I present folklore of the Iroquois, a northeast woodland people, and folklore of the Tohono O'odham ("Desert People"), a southwestern people. In Tucson I studied the language of the Tohono O'odham.

I continue to present keynote and storytelling programs for many venues (which include pow-wows starting with Gathering of the Tribes). I am also an illustrator of my stories and a yearly calendar with Native American themes.

Gil Payette
gil.address@gmail.com
518-279-3890

Changing Times

Based on an Iroquois Legend

Gil Payette

There was a man. He was an old man—and he lived to be a very old man. His hair was snow white, as were the skins, robes and feathers he proudly wore. His shoulders stooped just a little as he walked through the forest, beneath the cold gray-black clouds. Everything in his path turned to ice as he exhaled. He had taken many walks and now he felt his age. He was growing tired.

Four full moons ago this old one had caused the leaves on the trees to wither and die. Soon after, most of the birds fled from him, escaping to the south. Deer had retreated deep into the forest to avoid his wrath. Even mighty Bear could not deal with this harsh old man; instead, Bear would find a den and hide.

So few appreciate the old man's gifts to their lives.

When the old man stays in the land of the Iroquois, his only friend is the North Wind. They sit together and talk and laugh for days on end, but only about matters of winter and cold—never, never do they mention summer or warmth.

Again the old man walks through the forest and he notices a crack in the ice on the river. He tries to blow his cold breath to seal this crack—but all he can manage is a few short puffs of air. His old body cannot complete the task anymore. So he calls the North Wind to come and close the fracture. Then on his way back to his lodge the old one sees that the snowdrifts are getting smaller. He is growing weary—soon he will have to give up.

Early one morning a handsome young man dressed in brilliant green and gold comes to the old man's lodge. The young one has come for the old one to take him on his last walk. The very old man is barely moving even with the aid of his staff. He slowly follows the young one into the forest. As the old man shuffles along, the sun comes out from behind the clouds. They walk on—the new day warms...The old man is uncomfortable, he stumbles, his breathing is labored, he staggers and collapses. The young man just looks ahead and does nothing to help the old one.

Behind the two men the snow is melting and, in the imprints of their moccasins, wild flowers spring to life. The young one speaks and says good-bye to his old friend.

Old Man Winter has been vanquished by Young Man Spring. But winter will return again as soon as it is time for the seasons to renew the Circle of Life. And so be it.

It Is a Dog

Based on a Tohono O'odham Folktale

Gil Payette

A long time ago, before what is called history, the people of this land believed we were all related—the humans, the animals and the plants—all related through Mother Earth.

Some of these people were very close to one of the animals. This animal lived with the people in their lodges. Watched over the children. Guarded the villages. Was a beast of burden and went with the hunters and the warriors. Who was this animal? It was a dog.

When the Spanish Conquistadors came to the southwest, they brought many things and they took many things. One of the animals they brought with them was the horse. People here had domesticated the dog and it was thought that these horses were dogs of great size. Some called the horses Spirit Dogs. Soon many of the people became better horsemen than the Spanish themselves. With this horse many things changed. People with horses could travel longer, further and faster to attend gatherings, councils and dances. And their dogs traveled with them.

If you have ever had a dog friend you know that what you do, your dog wants to do. And so it was back then. What the people did, the dogs learned to do. The people would drum, sing and dance in circles—the dogs would bark, howl and turn in circles.

The people would have other tribes join them around their fires. And the dogs would have other canines join them. The dogs would be with wolf, fox and coyote. They would dance around their fire. It is sometimes said that coyote's black-tipped tail is because coyote burnt his tail by dancing too close to the fire. After that, when the dogs danced around their fire they would remove their tails and hang them on the greasewood bushes, on the ocotillo shrubs and on the saguaro cacti.

One night a noise from strangers alerted the dogs—they went to tell their people there might be danger. Each dog ran by the bushes, shrubs and cacti to get their tails. But in the confusion each dog grabbed another dog's tail.

And that is why today you see dogs whose bodies and tails don't match. Some big dogs have very small tails. Some short-hair dogs have bushy tails. Some dogs' heads and bodies are different colors than their tails. That is why dogs go around sniffing at each other's tails—they want their own tails back.

And now, my cousins, you know something about who dogs are and why dogs sniff. It is because they are dogs.

Snake Is Dying

Based on a Tohono O'odham Folktale

Gil Payette

There was a time when animals talked to each other. They even held council and talked about their relationships with Mother Earth and each other. Many came to these gatherings to hear the great ones speak. The most influential were Bear, Buffalo, Eagle and Snake. Bear has a great spirit; Buffalo has great strength; Eagle flies higher than any winged creature; Snake is very powerful and knows the mysteries of the desert. Snake called for the great ones, the mystics, the holy ones, and the healers to come and have talks with him. For four days they talked with Snake and on the fourth day Snake came out to all those waiting and told them his time with them was limited. He must prepare himself to join those of the Sky World. Snake was dying. Snake's family did what they could. Snake's friends, Jackrabbit, Desert Tortoise and Coyote, offered to help any way they could with whatever he wanted. Snake asked for a place to spend his last days, to be in his beloved desert, to see in all four sacred directions but to be in the shade.

The first to speak was Desert Tortoise. Tortoise wanted to dig a depression or shallow hole. The Tortoise Clan had always used these as shelters, so this is what they did for Snake. When Snake was brought to see the shallow resting place he was moved by what his friends did but from the hole he could not see in all four sacred directions.

Jackrabbit spoke next about his father and his father's father resting under a bush as a shelter or windbreak. But for Snake they would not use a bush or a shrub; they would use a Mesquite Tree. Again Snake was pleased his friends cared so much but near the base of the tree trunk he could not see in all four sacred directions.

Coyote has been on this Earth since the creation and has seen people live in cliff dwellings, pit houses, tepees, wickiups and longhouses, but for Snake, they would build a structure with four corner posts and a roof, but no walls. It would be called a watto [wa tah'] for shade. Snake saw this watto, this resting place in the shade, and cried because of what his friends had done for him. This is where Snake spent his last days. When Snake died, he was buried in the shallow hole, covered with rocks. A memorial was made at the Mesquite Tree and it was filled with prayer sticks. Snake's family and friends gathered under the watto to remember Snake. It was this way for many years.

One day humans saw the shallow, the wind break and the structure—they did not know what this place was but they knew it was special. They respected this place and returned to their settlement. They remembered the structure. They built some and sat under them in the shade to talk with their friends and to look out at their beloved desert. There was a time when the Spanish came; they too remembered the people's structure and built some of their own. The Spanish call this structure ramada for resting place. In the southwest, we have them everywhere, so you can sit in the shade and talk with your friends about your relationship with Mother Earth and one another.

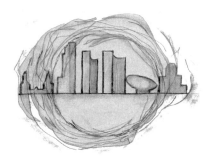

Sandor (Sandy) Schuman

My father was a storyteller. It was his everyday way of communicating ideas and values. I followed his example but didn't realize it until several years ago. After leading a three-day training program, I read the attendees' evaluation forms. In response to the question, "What did you like best about the program?" several people responded, "Sandy's stories." I didn't understand what they were talking about until my co-trainer pointed out several stories I'd told. Since then I've told stories more intentionally and in public performances where I tell personal adventures, historical sagas, tall tales, and Jewish stories.

Sandy has performed at Sharing the Fire: The Northeast Storytelling Conference, Limmud Boston, Caffè Lena, Tellabration, Word Plays at Proctor's Theatre, Story Sundays at Glen Sanders Mansion, and many storytelling festivals, professional conferences, interfaith events, churches, synagogues, radio, and television programs.

His book, *Adirondack Mendel's Aufruf: Welcome to Chelm's Pond*, was described by one reviewer as "sweet without being soppy, funny without being mean, and inspirational without being preachy." It's where the foolish stories of Chelm meet the tall tales of the Adirondacks.

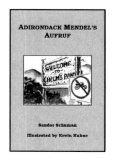

Sandor Schuman
www.tothestory.com
sschuman@exedes.com
518-229-8345

136

It's Hard to Tell a Hug

Sandor Schuman

My father was a storyteller. It was his everyday way of communicating. I discovered that I too am a storyteller. I have retold his stories and told my own stories about him. I told so many stories about my father—and then it dawned on me. I wasn't telling any stories about my mother. I began to feel bad. Surely, she deserved to have stories told about her. I thought about it. Why wasn't I telling any stories about my mother? I didn't have any stories about my mother! My father was a storyteller, so it was easy to tell his stories, but my mother was not. And while it's easy to tell a story, it's hard to tell a hug.

When I was four years old my mother asked me for the very first time if I wanted to stay home alone. My three older sisters were at school; my father was at work; I was home with my mother, and when she had to run an errand, I had to go with her. That was just the way it was. But here, for the first time, she said, "I have to go shopping. Would you like to stay home or do you want to come with me?" I used to get a headache going shopping—what am I saying, I *still* get headaches going shopping—so I said, "I'll stay home."

As soon as she left, I wanted my mommy. I thought, *Maybe she'll come back for her keys.* She was always forgetting her keys. So I put on my coat—she had bought me this dressy, full-length coat. And it was itchy wool that I hated. It was a black and white weave with a matching hat. I pulled that hat over my head and the earflaps over my ears and I tied that itchy wool string under my chin—I hated that hat more than the coat—and I stood there in the middle of the living room waiting for my mommy.

When finally she returned, she opened the door, saw me standing there in the middle of the living room with my hat and coat on, and instinctively, intuitively, she knew exactly what was going on. She quickly leaned down to put her packages on the floor, rushed over to me, picked me up in her arms and hugged me, and I was … relieved. And I cried and she cried and her whole body shook. She was not a slight woman and when she held you and her body shook, you really knew it. After some time I regained my composure, and my mother regained her composure, so she put me back down and we went about doing our little-boy-and-mommy things.

When I was twelve years old my Boy Scout troop was going to summer camp for the first time. We went camping once a month religiously all through the school year but we had never gone camping during the summer, much less for two whole weeks. When I heard this in the beginning of the year, I really didn't believe it. I thought sure that, by the time the summer rolled around, for one reason or another this deal would have dissolved. To say that it was beyond my wildest dreams would suggest too high a degree of probability. It was just inconceivable, other-worldly, and I didn't take it seriously until that day my parents drove me to the Port Authority Bus Terminal with my foot locker and my backpack and I joined my fellow scouts on the bus to the Ten Mile River Boy Scout Camp in the Catskill Mountains. I didn't think about home once until the weekend in the middle of our two-week stay, when the camp had "Parents Day."

Our campsite was set along the sloping ground of a wooded hillside. At the top of the hill was the dirt roadway; a footpath led down the hill through the woods until you came to a level area. Here was a clearing with a huge boulder, our campfire circle, and also the main cabin, where the scoutmaster stayed. Then another long slope until the campsite leveled off again. That's where the lean-tos were, where all the boys stayed. We were down there, all the boys, expecting our parents to show up before long, and we were neatening things up, shaking the leaves out of our sleeping bags, trying to make it look like we were taking care of the place, when I heard this voice bellowing from the top of the hill.

"Schuman!!!"

And there was my mother, a large woman, impatient to see me, bounding down that hill. I strode up the hill to meet her and we met in that campfire area in the center of the camp. She put her arms around me and hugged me and—at this point I was tall enough to see eye-to-eye with her—I hugged her back. She sobbed and her whole body shook. And all I thought was, *The whole camp is looking at us.* But I wasn't going to let anyone know I was embarrassed. I wasn't going to push her away. I was … tolerant. I stood there hugging her until she regained her composure and then we went about doing our Boy-Scout-Camp-Parents-Day things.

I was seventeen when I went off to college, and I never did move back to my parents' house, nor did I come home to visit all that often—but when I did, I would come through that front door and, right there in the foyer, my mother would be waiting for me and she would take me in her arms and she would hug me. I would bend down a little to put my head next to hers and she would sob, keeping herself from crying out loud and her whole body would shake and we would hug each other, and I was … understanding. And then after a time she would regain her composure and we would go about doing our young-adult-son-and-mother things.

That was the way it was. It was like a ritual every time. No, that's not right, it's not right to call it a ritual. There was nothing prescribed or predetermined. It was the real thing. It was genuine each and every time.

I was 29 the beginning of that summer when my wife and I were going to get married. The wedding was scheduled for Labor Day. It would be in our house, so we spent the whole summer getting things ready—painting, renovating, buying new furniture, ordering wedding invitations, finding a caterer.

It was an evening in July when I got a call from my sister, Selma.

She had just come from the doctor with my mother. My mother hadn't been feeling well the past many months, maybe a year or more. She was tired. She had what she described as a "low-grade fever." She would go to the doctor, the same doctor she'd been seeing for decades, and he would say, "Annette, you're getting older, you're in your late sixties. You just have to take it easy. Take some aspirin. Rest. That's the way it is, Annette."

On this particular visit, the old doctor was out of town so she saw one of the new doctors, a younger man. He examined her, looked through her files, noted her history of breast cancer, and immediately ordered some tests. My sister Selma had just come back from visiting the doctor where he gave her the report. My mother had colon cancer and it had advanced into her kidneys and liver and the prospects were not good.

I listened without responding, the phone pressed hard to my ear. Selma had many details to relay and, hearing my silence, just continued. She said, "I asked the doctor if she would be able to make it to my little brother's wedding. My little brother, the youngest of the family, the baby, the only boy."

The doctor asked, "When is the wedding?"

Selma told him, "September."

He replied, "Early September, or late?"

My mother did make it to the wedding. She was in good spirits. The members of our two families gathered at our house and moved about from room to room to meet each other, talking and eating, while my mother greeted everyone as she sat there on our couch—our new, white, Haitian-cotton couch, the kind with that coarse cotton weave—in front of the windows in the living room. I can still see her sitting there, beaming at me.

After the wedding, just about every weekend, my wife and I made the three-hour trip from Albany to Maspeth, in the western end of Queens, to visit my parents, to see my mother, to help out, all the way until the next spring. She died on April fourth.

Two-and-a-half years later, we were about to have our first baby. We had firmly decided, if it was a girl, to name her Anna, after my mother Annette. But if it was a boy, we were unsure. We might name him Benjamin, after my uncle, or Paul, after my wife's uncle, both of whom had recently died. We had not decided, even right up until my wife was in labor. In the maternity ward of the hospital one of the interns asked, "And if it's a boy, what will you call him?"

She said, "Benjamin Paul."

That was the first I heard it. He was a big boy, nine pounds, six ounces, Benjamin Paul.

He was born in December, so he was just five months old the following spring when Mother's Day came around. Of course, for me, Mother's Day was not the same, and never to be again. I wondered, after all, if Mother's Day had been invented for the mother, or if it had been invented for the child.

This Mother's Day was special, my wife's first Mother's Day and Ben's too. My wife was enjoying the day—out of the house for a while—and I stayed home with Ben. We were in the living room, warmed by the sun streaming in the front windows, sitting on that white Haitian-cotton couch. Well, Baby Ben was pretty good at spitting up and I suppose that white couch had by that point acquired a somewhat mottled appearance.

He started to cry, so I picked him up and put him on my shoulder, with a diaper there to absorb the spit-up that I knew would be forthcoming. I held him there and patted his little back. He was quieting down and I was thinking. *Here's this little baby who's completely dependent on me. He can't take care of himself. Why, he can't even lift up his own head! Yet I love him.*

He fell asleep, his hefty little body a relaxed weight slumped over mine, his head heavy on my drool-soaked shoulder, while I tried to come up with an idea for what he should give his mother on this special day. But my thoughts returned to this person-to-be. *He's incapable of linguistic expression, completely helpless, taking everything and giving nothing. And yet I love him completely, without reservation, without qualification; complete, unadulterated, unmitigated, unalterable love. I love him more than the sun loves to shine.*

And in that moment, I realized how my mother felt about me. For the first time I knew what that hug meant. I cried out loud, "I didn't understand! I didn't understand, Mom! I'm sorry."

So Benjamin, in his wisdom, prepared a Mother's Day card. On the front cover it said, "My First Mother's Day," and inside:

For the times when I am waking but you are still asleep
And the times when I am cranky with my diapers in a heap
For all these times I won't recall, I'm just a baby boy
Life is simple, so direct, and because of you it's joy.

I love you Mommy, in my baby-boy way, and still, when I will grow
I'll love you Mommy yet someday in ways I don't yet know.

And it was signed:

To Mother on Mother's Day
Love, Benjamin, age five months

Ben now lives in Brooklyn and is a computer specialist for an insurance company. Sam, his younger brother, works as a paramedic in Amsterdam, New York, while he completes his bachelor's degree. Their little sister, Anna—named after my mother Annette and born April fourth, the same date my mother died—graduated from college and will begin her fellowship this fall at an environmental education institute. I don't see these children very often, but when I do, you can be sure I give each of them a hug. I wish there was some way I could just tell you what that hug really means. But it's like I said at the start. It's easy to tell a story, but it's hard to tell a hug.

Maggie Whelan

Maggie Whelan is the mother of 11 and grandmother of 18. A retired special education teacher from Albany whose passion is writing and helping others find joy and healing through writing, she has had numerous articles published. She was the featured writer in a recent book signing where she read her essay, *A Glance at Heaven* in *Chicken Soup for the Soul: Answered Prayers* and is anticipating another publication with *Chicken Soup for the Soul* about forgiveness. Maggie's writing has also appeared in *Angels on Earth*, the magazine published by *Guideposts*. Maggie has presented at The Arts Center of the Capital Region and the Young Authors Conference in Westchester County. Maggie enjoys sharing tales about her family, its joys and challenges. She has presented workshops on journaling, memoir and creative writing and has developed workshops on spiritual writing titled "Writing the Prayer of your Life" and "Writing the Covenant of Your Life." In addition, Maggie has developed the program "Journaling as a Way to Relieve Stress," to be used as a series of training sessions for agencies and businesses.

Maggie Whelan
Slingerlands, New York
mags9119@yahoo.com
518-489-9110

The Year Elmo Saved Our Christmas

Maggie Whelan

My daughter was only gone a year when Elmo saved our Christmas. Bridget was a shining light to our family and at six years old had touched many lives. She was born with spina bifida, making her paralyzed from the waist down, and was not given much hope for having any quality of life.

But Bridget had different ideas and was a courageous, funny and loving little girl. She taught everyone who met her that life can be happy no matter what kinds of challenges it hands you. One thing about her that I will always cherish is how she reacted to people and how people reacted to her. Each day when she came home from school in her little purple wheelchair, she would exit the bus on the handicapped lift and I would begin to push her towards the house. She would say, "Mom, wait, I want to tell Bill something." Bill was the bus driver who adored her. Bill would come closer and bend down to hear what Bridget had to say and she would whisper, "I love you." Bill would respond in kind and the next day the ritual would be performed again.

Another day, when she was five, I took Bridget to a clinic at the medical center. As we sat in the waiting room, the door opened and a man in an orange jumpsuit with handcuffs and shackles came in. He had two police officers with him. Everyone in the room averted their eyes. I looked at Bridget's face and could see she was wondering what this was all about. I dreaded what she might say. She looked at the man and said, "Hi!" His face just lit up. No one else in the room but Bridget acknowledged his existence. She shared her love with all she met.

It was a shock when Bridget died suddenly just before Christmas in 1993. Our family gathered on Christmas Eve for her funeral and to celebrate the gift she was to us. Needless to say, I was changed forever and there is an emptiness in my heart that will never fully go away.

The following summer, as I looked toward the holidays with dread, I decided that I needed to shop early so that when Christmas came my other children would not be disappointed. One day I came across an adorable Elmo doll that laughed when tickled. At that time, there was no shortage, no excess demand. After all, it was August. So I bought it, paying about $20. I wasn't even sure who I would give it to but I thought one of the kids would enjoy it.

Months later, I was watching the news with my son Matt when a story came on about "Tickle Me Elmo" and the lengths people were going to get one. I commented, "I have one of those." He was quite surprised and excited, explaining he could get $500 or more for it on the street. I said, "No, it's Christmas...that's not right." He thought I was crazy and we both forgot all about it.

On the morning of December 21, I woke up and wasn't sure how I was going to get through the day. I was paralyzed with sadness as this was the first anniversary of Bridget's death. I knew I would replay the horrible night in my mind, her struggle to breathe, the ambulance, the hospital and telling her brothers and sisters she was gone. The other children were the only reason I got out of bed that day.

As I sat drinking my coffee, Matt came home from the repair shop where he had taken a TV to be fixed. He said, "Hey, Mom, do you still have that 'Tickle Me Elmo' doll?"

He told me that the woman who owned the repair shop was asking everyone if they had any idea where she could get one. It was the only thing her four-year-old granddaughter had asked for from Santa. She would call her everyday and say, "Grandma, HoHo is bringing me 'Tickle Me Elmo'!" and break into little girl giggles. The woman was heartbroken and tried everything to find one—from checking newspaper ads to taking chances in raffles—with no success.

I turned to Matt and said, "Let's go for a ride."

I walked into the repair shop with Elmo in my arms and tears in my eyes. When the woman saw me carrying the only gift her granddaughter wanted for Christmas, she started to jump up and down, crying, and saying "How much do I owe you? What do you want for it? Thank you so much!"

I told her I didn't want anything but to make a little girl happy on Christmas. I explained about my own little girl and what joy it gave me to make a Christmas dream come true on this day. Although the rest of the day was a struggle, I held on to the look on that woman's face and the belief that there really is a Santa Claus. This one time, it was me.

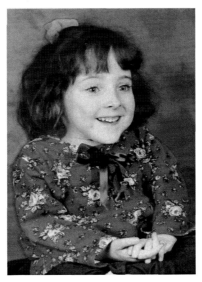

Uncle Tom and the Horse's Head

Maggie Whelan

When I think of the word "character," I immediately think of my Uncle Tom. He was actually my father's uncle, my grandmother's youngest brother, but everybody in the family called him Uncle Tom. His last name was Kennedy and he was known for the pride he had in his Irish heritage. Like many people of Celtic heritage, he loved to sing, dance, and tell stories. Tom was known for his sense of humor and practical jokes. They made him the favorite of many family members and the fear of many others.

I was a very young child when I visited him in his home where he lived with Aunt Celie and my cousin "Little Celie." (She is still known by that nickname even though she is well into her sixties.) His house was located in "Irishtown," near Bay Shore on Long Island. When we visited we would sit on his back porch. He and my father would drink, and laugh, and tell jokes that we were far too young to hear. So my brother Joe and I were banished to the backyard. There was a huge maple tree and we would chase each other and play tag.

One day I noticed a thick metal chain wrapped around the tree and asked Uncle Tom about it. He said, "Oh, that's where I used to have the lion tied up, but he got away." He said this with a serious face and I believed him. I was now afraid to go into his backyard and sat on the step of the porch, listening for any roaring that might come from behind that tree. I was ready to run and jump into my father's arms at any moment. Even as a teenager, when I understood teasing, I still walked hesitantly when I was in Uncle Tom's backyard. The chain stayed there for years and continued to be a favorite way for him to torment any child who was a visitor at his home.

When I was ten, Uncle Tom and Aunt Celie were at our home. We sat around the dining room table. The smell of alcohol and cigarettes filled the air. I was sneaking around hoping the adults wouldn't notice me and send me away. This day I was sitting off to the side. Uncle Tom turned to me and said, "What are you drinking?"

"Root beer," I responded.

"Really?" he said with surprise in his voice.

Hesitantly and not knowing what he was getting to, I admitted it. "Yes, root beer."

"Wow," he said. "You really like that stuff?"

Again I said, "Yes."

"Doesn't it make you have to go to the bathroom?"

"No," I assured him.

"Well," he said, "it makes me have to go. I wouldn't be surprised if you had to go any minute."

He said this with concern in his voice and a sparkle in his eye. He turned back to the adults and continued talking about the "good old days."

Within minutes I definitely needed to go to the bathroom. I waited as long as possible because I didn't want Uncle Tom to say anything and embarrass me in front of everyone. At ten years old going to the bathroom was humiliating, if everyone knew about it. When Uncle Tom was totally involved in an adult conversation, I got up very quietly and attempted to sneak out of the room. After my first step I heard this booming, singsongy voice, "I know where you're going!" I was devastated and I'm sure I was blushing.

As far back as I can remember Uncle Tom and my father had a healthy competition going. One day they got into a discussion about the proper way to fly the flag. It was not to be displayed before dawn and had to be brought inside at dusk, unless it was illuminated. They talked about not flying the stars and stripes in bad weather and how to properly handle and fold it. My father started to brag about how his flag was always out exactly at dawn on patriotic holidays. Tom joked saying he had driven past the house on the last Fourth of July as the sun was rising and the flag was not out yet. "Maybe you had a hangover that day!" he teased my Dad. Just to be sure that he was not outdone, on the next

149

holiday, my father checked to see exactly when the sun was going to come up. He set his alarm clock so he could be up and proudly put the flag out. That morning when he went out to the front porch, in the holder, where he was about to place the flag, sat a little note saying, "My flag is already out. Love, Tom."

My favorite Uncle Tom story begins when he was building his house in the 1950s in Bay Shore. As the contractors were digging the foundation, they discovered the skeleton of a horse. Since it was almost his sister Sadie's (my grandmother's) birthday, Tom immediately hatched a plan. He took the skull of the horse and put it in a large box, wrapped it in beautiful foil paper and added a huge shiny red bow. He kept it a secret from the rest of the family and no one was prepared for what would happen at Grandma's birthday party. Tom presented her with the gift and sat back with a smile on his face. Sadie oohed and aahed at what a beautifully wrapped present it was and how she hated to open it. Tom encouraged her as the entire family watched and wondered what surprise Uncle Tom had planned this time. When Sadie opened the lid of the box and looked inside she kept a straight face and said in a calm voice, "This is what I have always wanted." The whole family was thrilled that Grandma finally outfoxed Uncle Tom.

The "horse's head" started out as a joke and became a tradition. It was given as a gift and would show up at various family celebrations over the years. I don't remember who had it the year it wore an Easter bonnet and had decorated eggs placed in the eye sockets to celebrate the resurrection of Jesus from the dead. It sported an Irish derby with shamrocks strung inside and out on St. Patrick's Day. Birthday hats and balloons were found attached and it was always a surprise and an honor to whomever was the recipient. The last time it was decorated was when Grandma and Grandpa celebrated their fiftieth wedding anniversary. The horse's head was painted gold, wore a crown and had a "5" in the left eye socket and a "0" in the right. It was prominently displayed as a centerpiece at the party where the family gathered. Today, no one in the family knows where the horse's head ended up but I have a photo of my grandparents on that special day and it's the proof that Uncle Tom's horse's head really did exist.

Frank H. Wind

Frank H. Wind has been a storyteller since 2001, when he told the story of how he and his wife first met, at their wedding. Actually, Frank has been telling for far longer than that; he includes in his credentials the fact that he spent twenty-two years telling "stories" to management at work (he served as a micropaleontologist and reservoir geologist for Texaco USA before retiring in 1999). He offers a cornucopia of original and traditional stories, and often teams up with his wife, Dee Lee Wind, when they perform as "Frank-Lee Speaking."

Frank H. Wind
Castleton, New York
do_tell@verizon.net
518-458-1781

Columbus, We Have a Problem

Frank H. Wind

Can you imagine what it was like to have been at Kitty Hawk to see the Wright brothers ushering in the Age of Aviation?

I was at one such event where we witnessed history in the making. Back in 1969, I was one of about fifty scientists who witnessed what was probably the first and possibly the only time that an interstate bus traveled down the highway with the transmission changing gears in response to voice commands from the driver—a milestone in transportation history that few have ever heard of.

I am a retired geologist and, back then, I was in Columbus, Ohio to attend the annual meeting of the South-Central Section of the GSA, the Geological Society of America.

GSA meetings always have field trips the day before the start of the technical sessions, and I had signed up to take a day-long bus trip to see some of the local geology. For geologists with my key interests, stratigraphy and micropaleontology, the area south of Columbus is exciting, with excellent exposures of rocks from several key intervals in the geological record. The most spectacular stop on this tour was to be just north of Cincinnati at the Bear Creek Quarry.

Back then, US Highway 52 in southern Ohio was a narrow, two-lane road. To get into the quarry, you had to walk down a ramp that led from the highway, down into a jumble of mounds of discarded asphalt paving, sections of old sidewalk and occasional rusting car and truck bodies that populated the floor of the abandoned quarry. The ramp was steep, and the junction between it and the road was pretty sharp. The bus driver stopped on the side of the road and we all piled out and headed down the ramp toward the quarry face. We were first treated to a short description of the site by our trip leader, Dr. Walter Sweet from Ohio State. Then, on to the exposure. In front of us was a spectacular display of fossiliferous, thin-bedded limestone.

While we were all viewing and sampling this beautiful snapshot of ancient history, Sweet was approached by the bus driver. "Excuse me, Dr. Sweet. I need to talk with you. You see the bus?" He said this pointing to the bus now sitting on the ramp. "I was trying to turn around…The front wheels, they're on the ramp, but the rear wheels are in the air because the back end of the bus frame is caught on the edge of the road."

Sweet gave the driver a look of disbelief and the two men turned and slowly walked back towards the bus. The driver continued, "Even if I get free, I can't go further into the quarry with all these piles of junk down here."

Sweet thought for a moment, looked at the bus, then at the quarry face, at the bus, the quarry face. Then he smiled—maybe "grinned" is a better word—put his arm on the driver's shoulder and said, "Don't worry, Charlie, when we're finished, we'll get to work and have you out of here in no time flat."

After a few minutes, Sweet called us all together, apprised us of the situation and announced that we were going to get the bus off the ramp and out of the hole. But first, we had to reopen the quarry.

That we did. Teams fanned out and began carrying or dragging large slabs of limestone to both sides of the ramp. When it seemed as if we had enough, we were divided into two camps: "leaners" and "pavers." The "leaners" did as their name implied—they leaned on one side of the bus, raising the rear wheels on that side a bit further into the air. While the bus was leaning, the "pavers" built up the ramp surface from beneath the rear wheels, all the way to the top of the ramp. With one side done, we switched to the other. The builders of the pyramids would have been impressed.

It was a beautiful sight to see the bus backing out of the quarry and back on level ground. We all piled into the bus a bit tired, but exhilarated by our success.

Unfortunately, our success was only partial and our exhilaration short-lived, for when the driver tried to head us home, he discovered that in the process of getting out of the quarry, he had lost the ability to change gears from his seat. There was no way we would ever make it back to Columbus in reverse.

Ah, but all was not lost. The driver was thinking, *Ya know, there's an access panel on the floor opposite the rear door. If I can get that thing open*…He took a wrench out of his tool kit and removed the bolts. "You see those numbers…one, two, three?" He said this pointing into the murky bus innards. "If one of you boys would be so kind as to shift that lever when I call out, I think we can make it back by supper time."

So, with a rousing "Give me first!" and a "Give me second!" we headed home.

The Puzzle Wizard

Frank H. Wind

Every morning, I took the 6:55 into the City. I'd pick up a copy of *The New York Times* at the New Haven station, along with a bagel (poppy seed, lightly buttered) and a large coffee (sugar—two packets, no cream).

When you ride the New Haven line into the City, you tend to fall into a pattern. The same train, the same car—second from the rear—the same fellow riders: Steve Wishkowski, Lou Brown and Jeff Leeland.

A few of the riders would snooze on the way in, but most either pulled out paperwork from the office or read a book, magazine or newspaper. Some did a crossword puzzle, most often the daily *New York Times*, probably the most interesting and challenging around.

I would rapidly scan the newspaper to see if there was a report of something that might impact my life or the day ahead, then, on to the puzzle. I generally could do most of it, but ended up wrestling with clues like *seven letters, Greek philosopher*. I'd get as far as *p-something-o-c-something-something-s*. If I didn't give up, I would work on it the whole ride to Grand Central. I never tried the large puzzle in the Sunday magazine section. It was always too intimidating. Not all of it was over my head, but enough of the clues offered or answers sought were so esoteric that I was discouraged from even starting.

As we approached Grand Central Station, almost as if choreographed, those who were sleeping would arise from their slumber like zombies in a grade B movie. All of the papers and folders would be returned to the briefcases, the newspapers refolded, and the crosswords, if unfinished, torn from the papers and saved for later in the day, perhaps for the ride home. Then, both my newspaper and cup would be tossed into the trash barrel on the platform, and I'd be up the stairs and out into the morning sunlight to face the world, still wondering about *21 across, six letters, begins with an L, amino acid essential to animal nutrition.*

One Monday, we had a new traveling companion. He boarded at Milford, about eleven minutes into our run. He was tall, well-dressed, probably in his late 40s. He seated himself about three rows in front of me, on the north side of the car, opened his briefcase and took out the *NYT Sunday Magazine*. He opened it to the crossword puzzle and then took out, not a pencil or a thin-tipped ballpoint, my tool of choice, but a big, fat fountain pen. This was crazy! A fountain pen is totally unforgiving. Once it's down on paper, well, actually, it's in the paper. There's no room for change, no second opinion. It has to be right the first time. This guy was either a genius or a fool!

I tried to concentrate on the puzzle I was doing, but my eyes kept getting drawn to my fellow traveler. As we sped toward the city in the early morning light, picking up riders at Darien, Rye and the rest of the stations on the line, his puzzle became noticeably darker, as letter by letter, word by word, each vocabulary quiz was mastered.

Sometimes, after taking a sip from his coffee, he would rapidly fill in a whole cluster of words, finish off a corner or complete a pale section that had been crying for attention. He worked at an amazingly steady pace, but he occasionally paused to ponder a word or, I supposed, wrestle with a subtle or obscure reference. I was amazed with his progress. This guy was a genius.

Just as we left Melrose and the conductor chimed "Next stop Harlem-125th Street!" the puzzle master's pace quickened, and as we coasted into Grand Central, he filled in the last few squares, proudly viewed his accomplishment, then closed the magazine and returned it to his briefcase.

Tuesday morning our fellow traveler read some book—looked like a novel. He finished that and another book the rest of the week. No crossword puzzle. I guess that once you've beaten the Sunday monster, the dailies are so mundane, they're just not worth the effort.

Next Monday, he was back doing the Sunday puzzle again. I knew it was a killer. I now had my interest piqued and I had looked at it on Sunday—clues like *Son of Deucalion*. Again, he seemed to work right through it, occasionally pausing to ponder a nuance over his coffee or try out a word or two in the margin, then back to writing in the answers like a scribe or secretary taking dictation.

A couple of guys had moved forward to get better seats to observe this duel between the puzzle and the brain. On succeeding Mondays the audience grew so, at times, every seat with a clear view of the contest was taken. The train was never very full and he generally sat alone. His ability to best whatever challenges were thrown at him was uncanny and his Monday morning accomplishment, capped by that flurry of last minute completions as we entered Grand Central, mesmerized his mute rooting section.

Then, one Monday morning, about six months after he joined our run, we were delayed outside Grand Central due to a mechanical problem on the train coming down from Poughkeepsie. Distracted, he put the puzzle down on the seat and spent the next few minutes alternating peering out the window and checking his watch. When we finally made it into the station, a full 25 minutes late, he jumped out of his seat and was at the door before the train even stopped.

Now was our chance—to see and touch a masterpiece! I leaped forward and grabbed the magazine. *One across: common African antelope:* X-M-L-A-B-P. *One down: boisterous fun:* X-J-E-Z-L. For six months, this guy's been pulling our...*3 letter word for lower limb.*

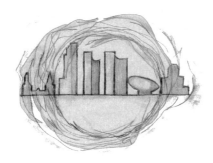

158